OXFORD

Maths links

Clare Plass

Contents

Homework Book

OXFORD
UNIVERSITY PRESS

Great Clarendon Street, Oxford OX2 6DP

Oxford University Press is a department of the University of Oxford.
It furthers the University's objective of excellence in research,
scholarship, and education by publishing worldwide in

Oxford   New York

Auckland   Cape Town   Dar es Salaam   Hong Kong   Karachi
Kuala Lumpur   Madrid   Melbourne   Mexico City   Nairobi
New Delhi   Shanghai   Taipei   Toronto

With offices in

Argentina   Austria   Brazil   Chile   Czech Republic   France   Greece
Guatemala   Hungary   Italy   Japan   Poland   Portugal   Singapore
South Korea   Switzerland   Thailand   Turkey   Ukraine   Vietnam

British Library Cataloguing in Publication Data

Data available

ISBN-13: 9780-19-915285-8
10 9 8 7 6 5

Printed in Great Britain by Ashford Colour Press Ltd.

Paper used in the production of this book is a natural, recyclable
product made from wood grown in sustainable forests. The
manufacturing process conforms to the environmental regulations to
the country of origin.

example

> Jane's children each grew a sunflower. These values are the heights that they recorded on a particular day in June.
>
> Alex 1.14 m   Jamie 140 cm   Matty 0.94 m   Andrew 1 m 4 cm
>
> Arrange these values in order of size, smallest first, and write whose sunflower grew the tallest.
>
> . . . .
>
> The values in metres are 1.14, 1.4, 0.94 and 1.04.
>
> In order these are 0.94, 1.04, 1.14 and 1.4 so Jamie had the tallest sunflower.

1 Write the value of these digits in the number 251.087.

   a 1   **b** 2   **c** 8   **d** 0

2 The number 3.45 stands for 3 units, 4 tenths and 5 hundredths. What do these numbers stand for?

   a 4.21   **b** 25.1   **c** 12.037   **d** 138.0604

3 Write each of these as a decimal number.

   a one ten, seven units and five hundredths

   b nine units, five tenths, one hundredth and three thousandths

   c one hundred, two tens, four units and seven thousandths

   d eight tenths and four ten-thousandths.

4 Increase these numbers by seven tenths.

   a 3   **b** 0.28   **c** 16.43   **d** 0.998

5 Decrease these numbers by five hundredths.

   a 6.48   **b** 2.35   **c** 12.64   **d** 0.205

6 Write each list of numbers in order, starting with the smallest.

a 8.4	8.3	8.28	8.35	8
b 7.8	7.86	7.81	7.08	7.818
c 5.92	9.52	5.29	52.9	0.529
d 0.42	1.4	1.042	1.204	0.142
e 0.003	0.03	0.036	0.603	0.063

1b Multiply and divide by 10, 100 and 1000

a Multiply 0.36 by **i** 10 **ii** 100 **iii** 1000
b Divide 24 by **i** 10 **ii** 100 **iii** 1000

You can use patterns to work out the answers to questions involving multiplying and dividing by 10, 100 and 1000.

a i $0.36 \times 10 = 3.6$ **b i** $24 \div 10 = 2.4$
  ii $0.36 \times 100 = 36$ **ii** $24 \div 100 = 0.24$
 iii $0.36 \times 1000 = 360$ **iii** $24 \div 1000 = 0.024$

1 Calculate
  a 34×10 **b** 8×1000
  c 12×100 **d** 4.1×10
  e 2.04×1000 **f** 45.2×100
  g 9.11×10 **h** 5.314×100

2 Calculate
  a $240 \div 10$ **b** $3500 \div 1000$
  c $650 \div 100$ **d** $4.1 \div 10$
  e $456 \div 1000$ **f** $992 \div 100$
  g $12 \div 10$ **h** $25 \div 100$

3 $\boxed{\times 10}$ $\boxed{\times 1000}$ $\boxed{\times 100}$ $\boxed{\div 100}$ $\boxed{\div 10}$ $\boxed{\div 1000}$

Write which of these operations must be applied to 3.056 to give
  a 305.6   **b** 0.3056
  c 3056   **d** 0.003 056

4 Write the operation that is needed to change
  a 2.56 to 25.6   **b** 56.12 to 0.5612
  c 0.35 to 0.000 35   **d** 314.3 to 0.3143
  e 1.052 to 105.2   **f** 15 to 0.15
  g 214.45 to 21 445   **h** 0.010 02 to 10.02

1c Negative numbers

example

Calculate   **a** -25 − -10   **b** 45 ÷ -9   **c** (-15)²

$$\begin{aligned} \textbf{a}\ &-25 - -10 & \textbf{b}\ &45 \div -9 & \textbf{c}\ &(-15)^2 \\ &= -25 + 10 & &= -5 & &= -15 \times -15 \\ &= -15 & & & &= 225 \end{aligned}$$

1 Put each of these sets of numbers in ascending order (lowest to highest).

a -2	-3	4	0	-7
b 12	-16	-23	31	-50
c -2	-6.1	-1.8	-6.4	-2.5

2 Insert a $<$ or $>$ symbol between each pair of numbers to make a true statement.

a 0 ☐ -3   **b** -6 ☐ 8   **c** -4 ☐ -7

3 Write the difference between these temperatures.

a -3 °C and 0 °C   **b** -1 °C and 8 °C
c 3 °C and -5 °C   **d** -12 °C and -7 °C
e -15 °C and 15 °C   **f** -18 °C and -21 °C

4 Calculate

a 7 − 10   **b** -5 + 6   **c** -12 + 4
d -4 − 2   **e** -9 + 9   **f** 20 − 40

5 Calculate

a 8 + -3   **b** 10 − 4   **c** -5 + 2
d 6 − -9   **e** -12 + -8   **f** -15 − -5

6 Find the missing numbers.

a -2 × -3 = ☐   **b** 12 × ☐ = -24   **c** ☐ ÷ 3 = -5
d -6 × ☐ = -30   **e** 16 ÷ -2 = ☐   **f** ☐ ÷ -50 = 2
g (-4)² = ☐   **h** 18 × ☐ = -9   **i** (9 ÷ ☐)³ = -27

1d Mental methods

example

a Use shopkeeper's subtraction to calculate $683 - 385$
b Use compensation to calculate $41.2 - 14.9$

- -

a Begin at 385 and count up to 683 in chunks.
$385 + \mathbf{15} = 400$ $400 + \mathbf{280} = 680$ $680 + \mathbf{3} = 683$
So, $683 - 385 = \mathbf{15} + \mathbf{280} + \mathbf{3} = 298$
b Subtract the nearest whole number and then compensate.
$41.2 - 14.9 = 41.2 - 15.0 + 0.1$ Subtract 15 and add 0.1 back on.

1 Calculate these using a mental method.
  a $32 + 18$ **b** $56 + 44$ **c** $84 - 14$ **d** $2.6 + 7.4$
  e $19.2 - 7.2$ **f** $12.4 + 7.6$ **g** $1.75 + 3.25$ **h** $11.75 - 6.25$

2 Use partitioning to calculate these mentally.
  a $4.1 + 5.8$ **b** $17.4 + 12.4$ **c** $24 - 14.6$ **d** $13.9 - 5.6$
  e $24.3 + 16.9$ **f** $8.3 - 5.8$ **g** $35.7 + 22.8$ **h** $45.4 - 17.8$

3 Use compensation to calculate these mentally.
  a $8.4 + 6.9$ **b** $44.5 + 12.8$ **c** $16 - 11.9$ **d** $45 - 13.95$
  e $29.35 + 17.95$ **f** $12.55 - 6.85$ **g** $14.73 + 9.85$ **h** $65.43 - 28.95$

4 Use 'shopkeeper's subtraction' to calculate these mentally.
  a $512 - 295$ **b** $934 - 475$ **c** $3264 - 1294$
  d $5276 - 2689$ **e** $8821 - 6543$ **f** $9549 - 4363$

5 Use doubling and halving to calculate these mentally.
  a 8×25 **b** 23×50 **c** 12×15
  d 19×25 **e** 9×45 **f** 32×15

6 Use compensation to calculate these mentally.
  a 32×19 **b** 21×39 **c** 45×21

example

Ben measures the perimeter of a rectangular picture frame as 1.84 m. The length of the frame is 0.64 m. Work out the width of the frame.

0.64 m

Two lengths are

$$\begin{array}{r} 0.64 \\ + 0.64 \\ \hline 1.28 \text{ m} \\ {}^{1} \end{array}$$

$$\begin{array}{r} {}^{7}{}^{1} \\ 1.\cancel{8}\cancel{4} \\ - 1.28 \\ \hline 0.56 \text{ m} \end{array}$$

Two widths are 0.56 m so one width is $\frac{1}{2}$ of 0.56 m = 0.28 m.

1 Calculate these using a written method.
  a 6.2 + 8.4   **b** 9.73 + 3.15   **c** 3.8 + 2.9
  d 5.36 + 4.94   **e** 1.2 + 7   **f** 3.05 + 8.3
  g 2.73 + 1.4   **h** 7.27 + 1.845   **i** 12 + 4.96 + 0.375
  j 0.455 + 32 + 16.29

2 Calculate these using a written method.
  a 24.1 − 11   **b** 43.7 − 22.4   **c** 31.2 − 25.4
  d 1.25 − 0.96   **e** 4.73 − 1.9   **f** 75.63 − 24.8
  g 15 − 5.2   **h** 6.8 − 3. 39   **i** 21 − 7.26
  j 42.1 − 5.328

3 Use a written method to solve these problems.
  a In the United Kingdom, life expectancy at birth is 81 years for girls and 76.6 years for boys. How much longer can a girl expect to live than a boy?
  b In 2005, the population of the United Kingdom was estimated as 60.2 million people, of which 50.43 million lived in England. How many people lived in other areas of the United Kingdom?
  c Kirsten and Steve have £40 to spend on a two-course meal. For the main course, Kirsten chooses the lamb at £15.95 and Steve chooses the salmon at £11.49. How much money do they have to spend on their desserts?

example

> Change this time in hours to a time in hours and minutes.
>
> | 5.2 |
>
> ·
>
> 0.2 hours = 0.2 × 60 minutes = 12 minutes

1 Remembering that, for example, 14.2 on a calculator means £14.20 when dealing with money, work these out.

   a The cost of 8 loaves of bread at £1.05 each.

   b The amount obtained by each person when a lottery win of £150 is shared equally between a syndicate of 12 people.

   c The cost of a class set of 30 pencils at 12p each.

2 Remembering that, for example, 28.4 on a calculator means 28 m and 40 cm when dealing with length, work these out.

   a The length in m and cm of five Ford Focus cars parked nose to tail if each car is 4.34 m in length.

   b The total length in m and cm of three friends laid head to foot on the ground if they measure 1.58 m, 180 cm and 1 m 65 cm.

   c The thickness in cm of a mathematics textbook if a pile of 30 textbooks has a height of 0.75 m.

3 These calculator displays give times in hours. Change them to hours and minutes.

   a | 7.25 | **b** | 2.1 |

   c | 4.333333333 |

4 Write a mental estimate for each of these calculations and then use a calculator to work out the exact answer.

   a $3.9 + 6.15 - 4.84$ **b** $31.35 - (8.18 \times 3.2)$ **c** $\dfrac{19.8}{4.4} + 3.61$

   d $(2.1)^3$ **e** -3.24×-1.96 **f** $-25.99 - -14.38$

> **example**
>
> This is a linear sequence.
> 3, □, 17, 24, 31, …
> Find the missing value.
> ·
> The sequence increases in jumps of 7.
> $(17 + 7 = 24, 24 + 7 = 31)$,
> The missing value is $3 + 7 = 10$.

1 Copy each of these sequences and find the next two terms.

   a 3, 6, 9, 12, 15, …   **b** 4, 9, 14, 19, 24, …

   c 50, 46, 42, 38, 34, …   **d** 26, 20, 14, 8, 2, …

   e 3, 3.3, 3.6, 3.9, 4.2, … **f** 1000, 100, 10, 1, 0.1, …

2 Look at this number pattern.

$$2 \times 9 = 18$$
$$22 \times 9 = 198$$
$$222 \times 9 = 1998$$
$$2222 \times 9 = 19\,998$$

   a Write the next two lines in this pattern. Use your calculator to check your answers.

   b By relating the number of digits that are 2 in the question to the number of digits that are 9 in the answer, write the answer to $22\,222\,222 \times 9$.

3 Describe the rule for each sequence in words and find the missing values.

   a 2, 9, □, 23, 30, …   **b** □, 7, 11, 15, 19, …

   c 2, $2\frac{1}{2}$, 3, □, 4, …   **d** 7, □, -3, □, -13, …

example

Find the position-to-term rule for the sequence
5, 14, 23, 32, 41, …
and use your rule to find the 100th term.

Each pair of terms has a difference of 9. This means that
the rule is 'Multiply by 9 and add or subtract something'.

Position	1	2	3	4	5
Multiply by 9	9	18	27	36	45

So the position-to-term rule is 'Multiply by 9 and subtract 4'.
The 100th term is $100 \times 9 - 4 = 896$.

1 Generate the first five terms of the sequences described
by these position-to-term rules.
  a Add 1 to the position   **b** Multiply the position by 5
  c Multiply by 3 and add 2   **d** Divide by 3 and add 1
  e Multiply the position by itself and then by itself again.

2 For each sequence, complete this position-to-term rule 'Multiply
by ☐ and add ☐.'
  a 4, 7, 10, 13, 16, ….   **b** 11, 13, 15, 17, 19, ….
  c 7, 12, 17, 22, 27, ….   **d** $1\frac{1}{2}$, 2, $2\frac{1}{2}$, 3, $3\frac{1}{2}$, ….

3 Generate the first term and the 100th term of the sequences
defined by each position-to-term rule.
  a 'Position subtract 10'
  b 'Multiply the position by 4 and add 3'
  c 'Add 8 to the position and divide by 2'
  d 'Multiply the position by itself and then by itself again'

4 Find a position-to-term rule for each of these linear sequences.
  a 3, 6, 9, 12, 15, …   **b** 1, 4, 7, 10, 13, …

2b² Sequence notation

example

Generate the first five terms of the sequence defined by
$T(n) = 5(n - 1)$

· ·

$T(1) = 5 \times (1 - 1) = 0$
$T(2) = 5 \times (2 - 1) = 5$
$T(3) = 5 \times (3 - 1) = 10$
$T(4) = 5 \times (4 - 1) = 15$
$T(5) = 5 \times (5 - 1) = 20$

1 Write a sentence starting with 'I think of a number...' to describe
each of these expressions.

  a $5n$ **b** $2n + 5$ **c** $\dfrac{n}{2}$ **d** $\dfrac{n}{3} + 1$ **e** $2(n + 7)$

2 Generate the first five terms of the sequences given
by these position-to-term rules where n is the position
and T is the term.

  a $T(n) = n + 3$ **b** $T(n) = 8n$
  c $T(n) = 2n + 5$ **d** $T(n) = 4(n - 1)$

3 The position-to-term rule of a sequence is
$T(n) = 10n + 5$. Find

  a the first term ($n = 1$)   **b** $T(7)$
  c the 10th term   **d** the 100th term.

4 Which of these sequences have the smallest 10th term?

  n^2 $3(n + 4)$ $\dfrac{n}{2} + 1$ $7n - 5$

example

A linear sequence has third term 28 and fifth term 44.
What is the first term?
. . . .
Each consecutive pair of terms has the same difference.
There are two differences between the third and fifth terms.
$44 - 28 = 16$ so one difference is 8.
So the sequence is 12, 20, 28, 36, 44. The first term is 12.

1 Copy and complete the table to find the position-to-term rule in words and in symbols for the sequence 8, 11, 14, 17, 20, ...

Position	1	2	3	4	5
Multiply by ☐	3	6	9		
Add ☐					

2 Using the method in question **2**, find the position-to-term formula for these linear sequences.

    a 4, 8, 12, 16, 20, ...   **b** 10, 20, 30, 40, 50, ...
    c 3, 5, 7, 9, 11, ...   **d** 5, 11, 17, 23, 29, ...

3 Choose one of these nth terms for each of these sequences.

 n^2 $n + 3$ $5n - 2$ $10 - n$ $2n$ $4n + 3$

    a 4, 5, 6, 7, 8, ...   **b** 2, 4, 6, 8, 10, ...
    c 7, 11, 15, 19, 23, ...   **d** 3, 8, 13, 18, 23, ...
    e 9, 8, 7, 6, 5, ...   **f** 1, 4, 9, 16, 25, ...

4 A linear sequence has second term 7 and fourth term 13.
    a What is the first term?   **b** What is the 100th term?

example

Fences are constructed with posts and crossbars. Find a position-to-term rule that connects the number of posts (p) with the number of crossbars (C).

The number of crossbars increases by 3 each time because each pair of posts needs 3 crossbars to join them. The rule is 'Multiply the number of posts by 3 and subtract 3'.

Posts (p)	1	2	3	4	5
Multiply by 3 and subtract 3	0	3	6	9	12

So the position-to-term rule is $C = 3p - 3$.

1 Here is a pattern of dots.

a Write the number of dots needed in patterns four and five.

b Copy and complete the table to find the position-to-term rule.

Position	1	2	3	4	5
Multiply by ☐ and add ☐					
Number of dots	3	5	7		

c Explain why your formula works.

2 A shopkeeper stacks tins of food in these patterns.

a Copy and complete the table.

Number of rows high (r)	1	2	3	4	5
Number of tins (T)	1	4			

b Find a formula connecting the number of rows and tins.

c Use your formula to work out the number of tins in a stack 20 rows high.

Vikram is using the function $y = 3(x - 2)$ and gets an output of 42. Draw an inverse function machine to find his input.

The opposite of 'Subtract 2 and multiply by 3' is 'Divide by 3 and add 2' or $y = \frac{x}{3} + 2$.

Input $= \frac{42}{3} + 2 = 16$

1 Copy the tables and fill in the missing function values.

Multiply by 4 and add 7	
Input	Output
1	
9	
	47

Subtract 3 and divide by 4	
Input	Output
3	
	4
21	

2 These cards show some outputs of functions.

12   13   15   20   11   24

Match each card with one of these functions if the input is 5.

a $y = 4x$ **b** $y = 2x + 1$ **c** $y = x^2 - 1$

d $y = 20 - x$ **e** $y = 2(x + 1)$ **f** $y = 3x - 2$

3 What function maps these inputs to these outputs?

Input	Output
1	10
2	13
3	16

Input	Output
4	7
8	15
10	19

4 The output of the function $y = 4x - 3$ is 29.

Find the inverse function and calculate the input.

Mapping

Draw a table of input and output values for the function
$y = 4(x - 1)$ using inputs from -2 to 4.

Input	-2	-1	0	1	2	3	4
Output	-12	-8	-4	0	4	8	12

For example, if the input is 2 this maps to $4 \times (2 - 1) = 4$.
Use patterns to help you when completing these tables.

1 a Copy and complete this table of input and output values for
the function $y = 2x + 1$.

Input	0	1	2	3	4
Output					

b Copy and complete the mapping diagram.

2 Draw a mapping diagram for each function, using inputs
from -2 to 2.

a $y = 5x$ **b** $y = x + 10$ **c** $y = 4x - 9$

d $y = 3(x + 4)$ **e** $y = x^2 + 3$ **f** $y = \frac{1}{2}x - 1$

3 Find the function represented by this mapping diagram.

4 Which two of these functions are equivalent?

$y = 2x + 8$ $y = 2x + 4$ $y = 2x - 8$ $y = 2(x + 4)$ $y = 4x + 2$

Algebra Mapping   **13**

3a Perimeter and area of a rectangle

example

Calculate the **a** perimeter and **b** area of this rectangle.

9 cm

14 cm

....

a Perimeter = 14 cm + 9 cm + 14 cm + 9 cm
= 46 cm
b Area = length × width
= 14 cm × 9 cm
= 126 cm²

1 Calculate the **i** perimeter and **ii** area of each rectangle.

a

5 cm

9 cm

b

22 cm

14 cm

c

9.5 cm

12 cm

2 Calculate the missing lengths from each of these rectangles.

a

Area = 81cm² *h* cm

9 cm

b

Area = 50 cm² 4 cm

p cm

c

Area = 96 cm² *x* cm

12 cm

3 Calculate the perimeter and area of these shapes.

a

3 cm

5 cm

b

9 mm

2 mm

10 mm

6 mm

c

12 m

6 m

12 m

4 m

20 m

14   **Shape** Perimeter and area of a rectangle

3a² Perimeter and area of a triangle

example

Calculate the perpendicular height of this triangle.

height

Area = 216 mm²

24 mm

Area $= \frac{1}{2}$(base × height)

2 × 216 mm² = 24 mm × height

$\frac{432}{24}$ = height

So the height of the triangle is 18 mm.

1 Calculate the **i** perimeter and **ii** area of each triangle.

a

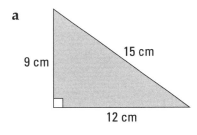

15 cm

9 cm

12 cm

b

13 m   13 m

12 m

10 m

c

13 mm   15 mm

12 mm

14 mm

2 Calculate the missing lengths on each of these triangles.

a

f cm   10 cm

X cm

12 cm

Perimeter = 27 cm
Area = 24 cm²

b

55 mm

Area = 825 mm²

y mm

3 Calculate the area of these shapes.

a

5 mm

8 mm

b

15 m

9 m

12 m

c

20 m

5 m

8 m

Shape Perimeter and area of a triangle   **15**

example

Calculate the shaded area of this shape.
....
The outer shape is a rectangle so its area
is $20 \times 10 = 200$ mm²
The unshaded area is in the shape of a
trapezium its area is $\frac{1}{2}(20 + 8) \times 10 = 140$ mm²

1 Calculate the area of each shape.

a

b

c

2 Calculate the area of each shape.

a

b

3 Calculate the missing lengths on these shapes.

a

b

4 A path crosses a garden as shown in the
diagram. Calculate the area of the path.

3c Surface area of a cuboid

example

A cube has a surface area of 541.5 cm². Calculate
a the area of one face
b the length of one edge.

. . . .

a Area of one face = 541.5 cm² ÷ 6
$$= 90.25 \text{ cm}^2$$
b Length of one side = $\sqrt{90.25}$
$$= 9.5 \text{ cm}^2$$

1 Pair up the cuboids that have the same surface area.
Show all your working.

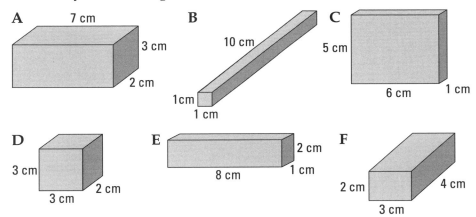

2 Calculate the area of one face of a cube with a surface
area of
a 96 cm²   **b** 37.5 m²   **c** 7350 mm²

3 Calculate the length of one edge of each cube in
question **2**.

4 Flora has a set of building bricks that measure 4 cm by
4 cm by 6 cm. How many of these bricks can she fit in a
box that has length 42 cm, width 16 cm and height 8 cm?

example

Calculate the height of this cuboid.

Volume = length × width × x

375 cm³ = 10 cm × 5 cm × x

$x = \frac{375}{50}$

= 7.5 cm

1 Pair up the cuboids that have the same volume.
Show all your working.

A 12 cm 5 cm 2 cm

B 3 cm 3 cm 8 cm

C 2 cm 9 cm 4 cm

D 8 cm 7 cm 5 cm

E 5 cm 8 cm 3 cm

F 7 cm 10 cm 4 cm

2 Calculate the missing lengths on each cuboid.

a 5 mm Volume = 30 mm³ x mm 2 mm

b 4 mm y mm 12 mm Volume = 168 mm³

c 3.5 m Volume = 42 m³ p m 1.5 m

d q cm Volume = 1331 cm³ q cm q cm

example

Calculate the unknown angle.

The known angles are 36° and 90°.
Angles on a straight line = 180°
$d + 36° + 90° = 180°$
$d = 180° - 36° - 90°$
$d = 54°$

1 Calculate the unknown angles.

a

b

c

2 Calculate the unknown angles.

a

b

c

d

e

f

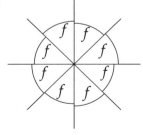

example

Find the angles of this triangle, giving reasons for your answers.

$a = 75°$ (alternate angles)
$b = 180° - 75° - 55° = 50°$
(angles on a straight line)
$c = 55°$ (corresponding angles)

1 Calculate the unknown angles, giving reasons for your answers.

a

b

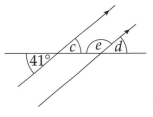

2 Calculate the unknown angles, giving reasons for your answers.

a

b

3 PQR and RST are triangles. PQ is parallel to ST. Give a reason for each answer.

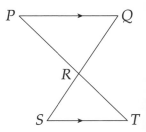

a Write an angle equal to PQR.
b Write an angle equal to QPR.
c Write an angle equal to PRQ.
d What have you shown about the angles of triangles PQR and RST?

example

Calculate the missing angles in this quadrilateral.

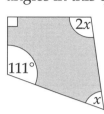

$2x + x = 360° - 90° - 111°$

$3x = 159°$

$x = 53°$

The angles are 53° and $2 × 53° = 106°$.

1 Calculate the unknown angles.

a

a $95°$ $69°$ $84°$

b
$2b$ $115°$ $95°$ b

2 Calculate the angles of these quadrilaterals, giving reasons for your answers.

a
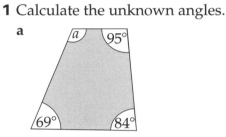

s r $52°$ q $100°$ p $81°$

b

$84°$ a b c d $77°$

3 Calculate the unknown angles.

a

$48°$ $85°$ a

b
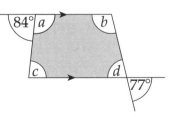

b $62°$ $73°$

4a Fraction notation

example

Write the angle 135° as a fraction of a turn.

One complete turn is 360° so

$$\frac{135}{360} = \frac{3}{8}$$

÷45 ÷45

1 Giving your answer in its simplest form, write the fraction of this rectangle that is shaded
  a black   **b** grey   **c** white.

2 Copy this rectangle and shade these fractions in the colour indicated.
  a $\frac{1}{3}$ in red   **b** $\frac{1}{6}$ in blue
  c $\frac{2}{5}$ in yellow   **d** Write the fraction that is unshaded.

3 Copy and complete these fraction equivalents.
  a $\frac{2}{5} = \frac{\square}{15}$ **b** $\frac{4}{9} = \frac{20}{\square}$ **c** $\frac{\square}{7} = \frac{6}{14}$ **d** $\frac{7}{\square} = \frac{56}{64}$

4 Write these angles as fractions of a turn. Give your answers in their simplest form.
  a 90°   **b** 270°   **c** 315°   **d** 225°   **e** 22.5°

5 The table shows the number of letters in the first 50 words in the children's book *Matilda* by Roald Dahl.

Word length	1	2	3	4	5	6	7	8	9	10

  a Write the fraction of the words that are 4 letters in length.
  b Write the fraction of the words that are not 5 letters in length.
  c How many letters are there in the words that occur $\frac{4}{25}$ of the time?

example

Calculate   **a** $\dfrac{3}{8} + \dfrac{2}{5}$ **b** $4\dfrac{3}{4} - 1\dfrac{1}{3}$

a $\dfrac{3}{8} + \dfrac{2}{5} = \dfrac{15}{40} + \dfrac{16}{40}$

$= \dfrac{31}{40}$

b $4\dfrac{3}{4} - 1\dfrac{1}{3} = \dfrac{19}{4} - \dfrac{4}{3}$

$= \dfrac{57}{12} - \dfrac{16}{12}$

$= \dfrac{41}{12}$

$= 3\dfrac{5}{12}$

1 Find the missing number in these sets of equivalent fractions.

a $\dfrac{1}{4} = \dfrac{\square}{8} = \dfrac{5}{\square} = \dfrac{\square}{24} = \dfrac{15}{\square}$ **b** $\dfrac{3}{5} = \dfrac{\square}{15} = \dfrac{12}{\square} = \dfrac{\square}{40} = \dfrac{30}{\square}$

c $\dfrac{3}{7} = \dfrac{\square}{14} = \dfrac{15}{\square} = \dfrac{\square}{70} = \dfrac{60}{\square}$ **d** $\dfrac{7}{9} = \dfrac{\square}{18} = \dfrac{28}{\square} = \dfrac{\square}{81} = \dfrac{700}{\square}$

2 Change these improper fractions to mixed numbers.

a $\dfrac{7}{3}$ **b** $\dfrac{9}{2}$ **c** $\dfrac{11}{5}$ **d** $\dfrac{15}{4}$ **e** $\dfrac{43}{8}$

3 Change these mixed numbers to improper fractions.

a $1\dfrac{2}{3}$ **b** $3\dfrac{1}{8}$ **c** $2\dfrac{3}{4}$ **d** $1\dfrac{7}{10}$ **e** $4\dfrac{5}{6}$

4 Calculate these, giving your answer as a fraction in its simplest form or a mixed number.

a $\dfrac{3}{5} + \dfrac{1}{5}$ **b** $\dfrac{8}{9} - \dfrac{2}{9}$ **c** $\dfrac{3}{4} + \dfrac{3}{4}$ **d** $1\dfrac{1}{6} - \dfrac{5}{6}$ **e** $4\dfrac{2}{7} - 3\dfrac{3}{7}$

5 Calculate these. You will need to change one or both fractions to equivalent fractions.

a $\dfrac{1}{4} + \dfrac{5}{8}$ **b** $\dfrac{5}{6} - \dfrac{1}{3}$ **c** $\dfrac{1}{2} + \dfrac{1}{3}$ **d** $\dfrac{2}{3} + \dfrac{3}{4}$

e $3\dfrac{1}{2} - 1\dfrac{3}{5}$ **f** $1\dfrac{1}{3} + 3\dfrac{1}{2}$ **g** $4\dfrac{3}{8} + 1\dfrac{3}{4}$ **h** $2\dfrac{2}{5} - 1\dfrac{1}{6}$

example

Change these fractions to decimals. **a** $\frac{11}{40}$ **b** $\frac{5}{8}$

a $\times 2.5$ so $\frac{11}{40} = 0.275$ **b** $\frac{5}{8} = 8\overline{)5.000}^{\,0.625}$ so $\frac{5}{8} = 0.625$

$$\frac{11}{40} = \frac{27.5}{100}$$

$\times 2.5$

$$\begin{array}{r} 0.625 \\ 8\overline{)5.000} \\ \underline{4\,8} \\ 20 \\ \underline{16} \\ 40 \end{array}$$

1 Copy and complete the table.

Fraction	$\frac{1}{2}$		$\frac{1}{10}$	$\frac{3}{4}$			$\frac{1}{3}$	
Decimal		0.25			0.01	0.2		0.6

2 Pair these cards if the two numbers are equivalent. Do not use a calculator and show your working. Write the odd one out.

$\frac{7}{20}$ 0.9   0.8 $\frac{3}{25}$ 0.35

0.4 $\frac{4}{5}$ $\frac{9}{10}$ 0.12

3 Write each of these decimals as a fraction in its simplest form.
   a 0.6   **b** 0.03   **c** 0.45   **d** 0.625   **e** 1.56

4 Write each of these fractions as a decimal without using a calculator.

   a $\frac{2}{5}$ **b** $\frac{3}{8}$ **c** $\frac{11}{25}$ **d** $\frac{17}{40}$ **e** $\frac{4}{9}$

5 These are Michael's exam results. Write them in order, starting with the subject in which he scored the highest mark.

   Chemistry $\frac{32}{40}$ English $\frac{39}{60}$ Physics $\frac{36}{50}$ Mathematics $\frac{54}{70}$

4d Fraction of a quantity

example

Work out $\frac{7}{9}$ of $\frac{2}{3}$ of 162.

· ·

$\frac{1}{3} \times 2 \times 162 = \frac{1 \times 324}{3} = \frac{324}{3} = 108$

$\frac{1}{9} \times 7 \times 108 = \frac{1 \times 756}{9} = \frac{756}{9} = 84$

1 Calculate these mentally.

  a $\frac{1}{3}$ of 240   **b** $\frac{1}{4}$ of 90

  c $\frac{3}{4}$ of 36   **d** $\frac{3}{5}$ of 45

2 Use a written method to calculate these.

  a $\frac{2}{9}$ of £63   **b** $\frac{5}{12}$ of 120 m   **c** $\frac{3}{8}$ of 40 kg

  d $7 \times \frac{1}{3}$ **e** $\frac{5}{6}$ of $54   **f** $\frac{3}{11}$ of 132 km

  g $20 \times \frac{4}{9}$ **h** $\frac{2}{13} \times 104$

3 Isla bakes 36 fairy cakes. She covers $\frac{1}{4}$ of them in purple icing, $\frac{2}{9}$ of them in pink, 11 in pale blue and all the rest in chocolate except for one which is eaten by her mother.
  a Calculate the number of cakes that have purple icing.
  b Calculate the number of cakes that have pink icing.
  c How many cakes are covered in chocolate?

4 Work out $\frac{2}{5}$ of $\frac{1}{4}$ of 180.

5 Carbon-14 has a half-life of 5370 years. This means that after 5370 years half of the atoms have decayed.
How many years will it take for a quantity of Carbon-14 to become $\frac{1}{8}$ of its original size?

example

Change $\frac{1}{32}$ into **a** a decimal **b** a percentage using a calculator.

· ·

a Type [1] [÷] [3] [2] into your calculator. This gives 0.031 25.

b To change 0.031 25 into a percentage, type [×] [1] [0] [0]
giving 3.125%.

1 Pair these cards if they show equivalent
numbers. Which is the odd card out?

(75%) (1.75) (0.175) (7.5%) (17.5%)

(175%) (7.5) (0.075) (0.75)

2 Change these fractions into percentages.

a $\dfrac{3}{4} = \dfrac{\square}{100} = \square\%$ **b** $\dfrac{2}{5} = \dfrac{\square}{100} = \square\%$ **c** $\dfrac{7}{20}$ **d** $\dfrac{18}{25}$

3 Use a calculator to change these fractions to
i decimals
ii percentages.
Give your answers to 2 decimal places where appropriate.

a $\dfrac{13}{20}$ **b** $\dfrac{7}{40}$ **c** $\dfrac{11}{16}$ **d** $\dfrac{4}{9}$ **e** $1\dfrac{1}{3}$

4 Change these decimals to fractions in their simplest
form by first writing each one as a fraction out of 100.

a $0.26 = \dfrac{26}{100} = \dfrac{\square}{50}$ **b** $0.95 = \dfrac{\square}{100} = \dfrac{\square}{20}$

4f Percentages

Work out the cost of a four-bedroom detached house if the owners reduce the asking price of £445 000 by 14%.

14% of £445 000 = 0.14 × 445 000 = £62 300
So the new asking price is £445 000 − £62 300 = £382 700

1 Calculate

  a 50% of 125 m   **b** 25% of £150   **c** 10% of 14 litres

  d 20% of $165   **e** 30% of 1500 g   **f** 90% of € 200

2 Work out these percentages using a calculator.

  a Girls aged 11−14 require 1800 calories per day. Molly eats an Easter egg and immediately consumes 9.5% of her daily calories. How many calories are there in the Easter egg?

  b Johanna spends £24.40 on her meal at a French bistro. A 12.5% service charge is added to her bill. How much is the service charge?

  c A bank offers an account with an interest rate of 6.5%. John invests £3000. How much interest will he earn in one year?

3 Work out the cost of these sale items if they are reduced by 15%.

  a   **b**   **c**

£80

£45

£18.50

example

Aisling recorded the number of people in each of 15 teachers' cars arriving at school one Monday morning.

1 1 3 2 1 2 1 2 1 1 1 3 4 2 2

Find **a** the mode **b** the median **c** the range of this set of data.

a The mode is the most common result = 1

b Order the data to give 1, 1, 1, 1, 1, 1, 1, 2, 2, 2, 2, 2, 3, 3, 4 and choose the middle result. The median is 2.

c The range is 4 − 1 = 3

1 Copy and complete the table by placing each statement under the correct heading according to the type of data that it would generate.

Discrete	Continuous	Non-numerical

a The number of people waiting at a bus stop

b The colour of students' school bags

c The time taken to travel to school

d The number of heads when three coins are tossed

e The weight of apples picked from a tree

f The shoe sizes of primary school children

2 Find **i** the mode **ii** the median **iii** the range of these sets of data.

a 5, 8, 0, 8, 2

b 11, 15, 13, 10, 12, 19, 10, 12, 18

c -7, -5, 4, -1, 0, -7, -3

d 103, 108, 104, 104, 106, 109

3 These are some temperatures recorded at the Amundsen–Scott South Pole Station in Antarctica.

2 p.m. June 21	8 p.m. June 21	2 a.m. June 22	8 a.m. June 22	2 p.m. June 22
-50 °C	-51 °C	-47 °C	-46 °C	-45 °C

Find **a** the median **b** the range of this set of data.

example

> The total cost of five different types of washing-up liquid is
> £4.65. Calculate the mean cost.
> . . . .
> Mean $= \dfrac{£4.65}{5} = £0.93$

1 The total rainfall (in mm) recorded each March from 1998
to 2007 is listed below. Calculate the mean rainfall for March
during this period.

1998	1999	2000	2001	2002	2003	2004	2005	2006	2007
96.5	70.9	38.0	91.3	49.3	38.9	53.9	52.0	93.5	64.5

2 Niall recorded the time taken for a group of students
to complete a sudoku puzzle. The times in minutes are
Boys   34,   23,   19,   28,   32
Girls   27,   36,   28,   25,   30
  a Calculate the mean time taken for the boys.
  b Calculate the mean time taken for the girls.
  c Calculate the mean time taken for the whole group of students.

3 Caiomhe recorded the time taken by five of her friends to travel to
school one Friday morning.
The times in minutes are 11, 12, 9, 10, 58.
  a Calculate the mean time taken to travel to school.
  b Is this value a fair indicator of the time taken to travel to school?
     Explain your answer.

4 Orla scored these results in her end
of year examinations.
  a Calculate her mean score in maths,
     English and science.
  b When Orla receives her Spanish
     result, her mean score increases to
     75%. What is Orla's Spanish result?

Maths	75%
English	70%
Science	68%
Spanish	

example

The frequency table shows the numbers of letters in the first sixteen words of *Northern Lights* by Philip Pullman.

Number of letters	2	3	4	5	6	7	8	9

Calculate the mean number of letters.

The total number of letters is

$(2 \times 2) + (3 \times 4) + (4 \times 5) + (5 \times 2) + (6 \times 1) + (7 \times 1) + (9 \times 1)$
$$= 4 + 12 + 20 + 10 + 6 + 7 + 9$$
$$= 68$$

The mean number of letters is $\frac{68}{16} = 4.25$

1 A group of children conduct a survey on the number of doors on the cars that pass their school gate in a 20-minute period. These are their results.

2 4 3 3 2 5 2 4 3 4 5 4 5 3 5 5 4 2 3 5 3

a Copy and complete this frequency table.

Number of doors	2	3	4	5
Frequency				

b Write the two modes.

c Calculate the range.

d Calculate the median number of doors.

e Calculate the mean number of doors.

2 These are the numbers of letters in the first twenty words of the children's novel *Anne of Green Gables* by L. M. Montgomery.

3 6 5 5 4 5 3 7 4 4 6 4 4 1 6 6 7 4 6 3

a Show this information in a frequency table.

b Write the modal number of letters.

c Calculate the median number of letters.

d Calculate the mean number of letters.

5d Frequency diagrams

example

The table shows where people consult their doctor. The numbers are percentages.

	1975	2005
Surgery	78	87
Telephone	3	10
At home	19	3

a Draw a comparative bar chart to represent this information.

b Describe the change from 1975 to 2005.

a

b In 1975, it was much more commonplace for doctors to make home visits. In 2005, telephone calls seem to have replaced these home visits and more people make the journey to the surgery.

1 The table gives the average cost, in pence, of some basic household items in 1996 and 2006.

	1996	2006
250 g Cheddar cheese	115	142
12 size 2 eggs	158	181
800 g white bread	55	81
1 pint milk	36	35
1 kg sugar	76	74

a Draw a comparative bar chart to represent this information.

b Compare the cost of these basic household items over this ten-year period.

example

The pie chart shows the dessert choices of some friends at a party.

Eight friends chose the chocolate mousse.
Work out the number of friends that chose the other two options.

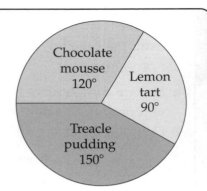

· ·

120° represents 8 friends so 120° ÷ 8 = 15° represents 1 friend.
Lemon tart was chosen by 90° ÷ 15° = 6 friends.
Treacle pudding was chosen by 150° ÷ 15° = 10 friends.

1 This pie chart shows the proportion of each ingredient required to make shortbread fingers.
  a Write the fraction of the recipe that is butter.
  b Write the fraction of the recipe that is sugar.
  c Doris wants to make 450 g of this mixture. Calculate the amount of each ingredient she needs.

2 The Key Stage 3 Mathematics SATs results for St. Clare's School are given in this pie chart.
  a Work out the angle representing 'Level 5'.
  b 24 students achieved Level 6. Work out the number of students taking SATs in St. Clare's School.
  c Calculate the number of students

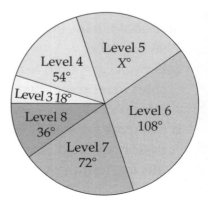

example

This table gives information about the average class size in England at Key Stage 2 during the period 1998 to 2005.

1998	1999	2000	2001	2002	2003	2004	2005
28.3	28.4	28.3	27.9	27.4	27.3	27.2	27.3

Draw a time series graph and comment on any trends shown.

The average class size has decreased on the whole, although not dramatically.

1 A waiter kept a record of his tips over a 12-month period, in pounds per month.

Jan	Feb	Mar	Apr	May	Jun	Jul	Aug	Sep	Oct	Nov	Dec
40	40	48	70	75	92	100	120	85	56	45	104

a Draw a time series graph to represent this set of data.

b Comment on the trends shown.

2 The table shows the temperature in °C taken each hour on 8 July 2007 at Wick, and Camborne.

	10.00	11.00	12.00	13.00	14.00	15.00	16.00	17.00
Wick	12	13	13	14	14	14	15	15
Camborne	17	17	15	16	16	15	17	16

a Plot line graphs for this data on the same set of axes, remembering to join the points with broken lines.

b Describe the behaviour of the temperature in Wick and Camborne on 8 July 2007.

c Explain why your graph cannot give the temperature in Wick at 14.30.

example

Grace and Isobel both substitute $p = 5$ into the expression $2p^2$.
Grace gets 50 and Isobel gets 100. Who is correct?

....

Grace is correct as she has worked out $2 \times 5^2 = 2 \times 25 = 50$.
Isobel has worked out $2 \times 5 = 10$ and then squared her answer
to get 100. BIDMAS reminds us to calculate indices first.

1 Write an algebraic expression for each of these.
   a Jason has x pounds in his bank account. He deposits
   £5. How much money is in his account now?
   b There are 12 birds sitting on a streetlight. y birds fly
   away. How many birds are there on the streetlight now?
   c Victoria puts k cakes onto each of her three friends'
   plates. She then adds another cake to each plate.
   How many cakes has she used?
   d Alexander paints m pictures. In each picture there
   are n trees. How many trees has he painted?

2 Given that $x = 2$ and $y = 8$, find the value of these expressions.
   a $x + 10$ **b** $y - 3$ **c** $2y$
   d $\dfrac{y}{x}$ **e** $2y + 3$ **f** xy
   g $3(x + 1)$ **h** $x^2 + y$

3 Match one of these number cards with each of these
   expressions, given that $a = -2$.

   4   −6   8   −8   1   6   −4   −1

   a a^2 **b** $2a + 5$ **c** $2a$
   d $\dfrac{a}{2}$ **e** $5a + 2$ **f** $a^3 + 2$

Which of these expressions is equivalent to $3x^2 - x - 6 - x + 6$?

$3x^2 - 12$ x^2 $3x^2 - 2x$

$3x^2 - x - 6 - x + 6 = 3x^2 - x - x + 6 - 6$
$= 3x^2 - 2x$

1 Simplify these expressions.

a $x + x + x + x$ **b** $3a + 4b$

c $2 \times y$ **d** $a \times a$

e $9k - 4k$ **f** $8p + 3p - 5p$

g $4m - 2m + 3$ **h** $12b + 3c - 4b + 5c$

i $5p - 4q + p$ **j** $2t + 8t^2 - 2t$

k $4ab + 8ab - 3ba$ **l** $\frac{1}{2}(6n - 4n^3)$

2 Sort these cards into pairs of equivalent algebraic expressions. Show all your working.

$3p + 3p + 4p$ $pq + 7$ $3pq + 4qp$

$q - q + p - 7q$ $7 \times q \times p$

$5p + 2q + 5p - 2q$ $-7q + p$ $4pq - 3pq + 3 + 4$

3 Show that the perimeters of these shapes are equal.

> ### example
>
> Expand and simplify this algebraic expression.
> $3(x + 5) - 2(x - 3)$
>
> $$3(x + 5) - 2(x - 3) \qquad = 3x + 15 - 2x + 6$$
> $$= 3x - 2x + 15 + 6$$
> $$= x + 21$$

1 Expand these brackets.

   a $2(x + 4)$ **b** $3(y + 2)$

   c $5(p + 10)$ **d** $4(q - 1)$

   e $a(b + 5)$ **f** $x(y - 8)$

   g $m(12 - n)$ **h** $a(a + 7)$

   i $2x(x + y)$ **j** $3p(6 - 2p)$

2 Expand these brackets and simplify where possible.

   a $2(x + y + 3)$ **b** $-4(a + 2b + c)$

   c $x(x + 3y - 1)$ **d** $4(a + 1) + 2(a + 3)$

   e $3(q + 6) + 4(q - 3)$ **f** $5(2x + 1) + 3(3x - 4)$

   g $2(t + 3) - 4(t + 1)$ **h** $a(a + b) + b(a - 2b)$

3 Write an expression for

   a the perimeter

   b the area of this rectangle.

$3a - 2$

4

4 Lily thought of a number, subtracted 2 and multiplied
it by 5. Gemma thought of a number, multiplied it by
5 and subtracted 10. Both girls got 20.

   a Find the number that Lily thought of.

   b Find the number that Gemma thought of.

   c What do you notice about these numbers?

   Will this always be true? If so, prove your answer using algebra.
Write an algebraic expression and expand the brackets.

Convert £120 to Australian dollars using the formula $D = 2.5P$ where D is the number of Australian dollars and P is the number of pounds.

. . . .

$D = 2.5 \times 120$ Substitute 120 for P.

$\quad = 300$

So £120 is 300 Australian dollars.

1 The perimeter of a square can be found using the formula $P = 4l$ where P is the perimeter and l is the length.

a Find P when $l = 6$ cm.

b Find the perimeter of a square with sides 8 mm.

c Explain why this formula works.

2 The mass(m) of an object is measured in kilograms and cannot change. The weight(w) of an object is measured in newtons (N) and depends on gravity(g). Gravity is measured in N/kg (newtons per kg). On Earth gravity is 10 N/kg and on Mars gravity is 4 N/kg. The weight of an object is found by multiplying its mass by gravity: $w = mg$

A person has a mass of 50 kg. Work out their weight

a on Earth

b on Mars.

3 A plumber calculates the cost to his clients using the formula $C = 45 + 9.5h$ where C is the cost in pounds and h is the number of hours he takes to fix a problem.

a Work out the cost of a job that lasts 2 hours.

b What is the plumber's call-out fee? Explain your answer.

6e Deriving a formula

example

Write a formula for the area of this parallelogram, expanding any brackets.

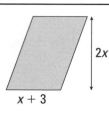

2x

x + 3

Area of a parallelogram
$$= \text{length} \times \text{height}$$
$$= (x + 3) \times 2x$$
$$= 2x(x + 3)$$
$$= 2x^2 + 6x$$

1 a How many edges are there on a cube? On five cubes?
  b Write a formula to find E, the number of edges on x cubes.

2 Philip is given £10 pocket money per week and £2.50 for each household chore that he completes.
  a Write a formula for M, the amount of money that he receives per week based on c, the number of chores that he completes.
  b Use your formula to work out how much money Philip receives if he washes his Dad's car and mows the lawn in one week.

3 The cost of spending 7 nights in a four-star hotel in Sorrento, Italy, is £560 per adult and £350 per child.
  a Write a formula for C, the total cost for a adults and c children taking this holiday.
  b Use your formula to work out how much this holiday would cost a family of 2 adults and 3 children.

4 One of the parallel edges of this trapezium is 3 times the length of the other.
  Write a formula for the area of this trapezium.

x

h

3x

> Substitute x and $3x$ into the formula for the area of a trapezium and simplify.

example

Work out   **a** 1.7×0.452 **b** $13 \div 17$
Give your answers to 2 decimal places.

. . . .

a $1.7 \times 0.452 = 0.7684$ The 8 tells you to round up.
So $1.7 \times 0.452 = 0.77$ (2dp)
b $13 \div 17 = 0.764\ 705\ 882\ ...$ The 4 tells you to round down.
So $13 \div 17 = 0.76$ (2dp)

1 Round each number to the nearest 10.

a 22	**b** 47	**c** 35	**d** 99
e 124	**f** 386	**g** 505	**h** 1523

2 Round each number to the nearest **i** 100 **ii** 1000.

a 672	**b** 949	**c** 1264	**d** 5889
e 3614	**f** 7250	**g** 28 410	**h** 65 525

3 Round each number to the nearest tenth.

a 2.83	**b** 4.17	**c** 3.64	**d** 0.79
e 16.22	**f** 6.45	**g** 21.045	**h** 0.95

4 Round each number to the number of decimal places given in the question.

a 1.35 (1dp)	**b** 0.268 (2dp)
c 17.6722 (2dp)	**d** 0.559 (1dp)
e 24.081 (1dp)	**f** 54.6575 (3dp)
g 37.595 (2dp)	**h** 8.4996 (3dp)

5 Convert each fraction into a decimal using a calculator. Give your answer to the nearest hundredth or use recurring decimal notation where appropriate.

a $\dfrac{4}{9}$ **b** $\dfrac{7}{16}$ **c** $\dfrac{23}{32}$ **d** $\dfrac{8}{11}$

7b Order of operations

example

a Insert brackets to make $9^2 - 21 \div 3 = 20$ true.
b What is the correct answer if no brackets are inserted?

a $(9^2 - 21) \div 3 = 20$
b $9^2 - 21 \div 3 = 81 - 21 \div 3 = 81 - 7 = 74$

1 Calculate

a $2 \times 3 + 6$	**b** $7 + 8 \div 2$
c $2 + 3 \times 5$	**d** $16 - 3 \times 4$
e $2 \times 5 + 6 \times 4$	**f** $24 - 9 \div 3$
g $4 + 18 \div 2$	**h** $14 \div 2 - 18 \div 3$

2 Calculate

a $4 \times (2 + 8)$	**b** $(16 - 8) \div 4$
c $(30 - 12) \times 2$	**d** $3 \times (9 - 4) \times 4$
e 5×2^3	**f** $4^2 + 21 \div 3$
g $\dfrac{6^2 + 4}{8}$	**h** $\dfrac{8 + (3^2 - 4)}{10}$

3 Copy these calculations and insert brackets, **if necessary**, to make the answers correct.

a $3 \times 9 + 2 = 33$	**b** $15 - 2 \times 3 = 9$
c $3 \times 5 + 2 \times 4 = 84$	**d** $8 + 24 \div 4 = 8$
e $8 \times 8 - 4 \times 3 = 52$	**f** $100 - 36 \div 4 = 16$
g $2^2 + 20 \div 5 = 8$	**h** $30 \div 6 - 2^2 = 15$

4 Use a calculator to work out these calculations. Where appropriate, give your answer to 2 decimal places.

a $(11 + 2.8) \div 3.1$	**b** $(3 - 2.8)^2 \times 1.56$
c $\dfrac{14}{9 \times 8}$	**d** $26 - 4.3^2 \div 3$

example

George sponsors Cristina 15p for every word that she spells correctly in a sponsored spelling test. Cristina spells 49 words correctly. How much does George owe her?

· ·

You need to calculate 15p × 49.

Using compensation you calculate $15 \times 50 - 15 = 750 - 15 = 735$

George owes Cristina £7.35.

1 Calculate these using factors.

   a 8 × 50   **b** 16 × 40   **c** 14 × 300   **d** 1.5 × 60

   e 3.2 × 30   **f** 4.4 × 500   **g** 2.25 × 40 **h** 1.75 × 800

2 Calculate these using the method of partitioning.

   a 11 × 3.8   **b** 14 × 5.1   **c** 15 × 2.4   **d** 23 × 1.5

   e 459 ÷ 9   **f** 328 ÷ 4   **g** 504 ÷ 6   **h** 504 ÷ 7

3 Calculate these using the method of compensation.

   a 22 × 9   **b** 35 × 19   **c** 28 × 21   **d** 17 × 31

   e 2.7 × 11   **f** 4.3 × 19   **g** 29 × 0.8   **h** 49 × 6.2

4 Use an appropriate mental method to calculate these.

   a Meredith is setting out the chairs for assembly. She has been asked to set out 21 rows of 24 chairs. How many chairs will she have to set out?

   b Derek spends £3.90 on his favourite monthly magazine. Calculate how much he spends on this magazine in one year.

   c Izzie records Dora the Explorer on to her hard drive recorder every day in April. Each episode uses up 0.9 GB of the space. If her hard drive recorder has 160 GB of space, how much free space will she have at the end of the month?

example

Work out 4.2×3.5.

Change the calculation to an equivalent whole number calculation. $4.2 \times 3.5 = 42 \times 35 \div 100$

$$\begin{array}{r} 42 \\ \times\,35 \\ \hline 210 \\ 1260 \\ \hline \end{array}$$

210 ⟵ 5×42

1260 ⟵ 30×42

So $4.2 \times 3.5 = 1470 \div 100 = 14.7$

1 Calculate these using a written method of your choice. Remember to estimate the answer first.

a 12×27 b 22×39

c 38×25 d 53×47

e 123×15 f 218×35

g 503×61 h 727×82

2 Calculate these. Remember to estimate the answer first.

a 6×9.4 b 15×7.3

c 26.2×8 d 3.43×46

e 2.6×5.8 f 6.4×3.2

g 4.9×2.5 h 8.02×7.5

3 a Charlie washes dishes at a hotel. He places the dishes in stacks of 24. At the end of his shift he has 18 stacks of dishes. How many dishes has he washed?

b A bed and breakfast charges £45 per person per night. Rebecca decides to stay for two weeks. How much will her stay cost?

c Gino charges £7.25 for one of his speciality cocktails. Each member of a party of 32 people drinks two of these cocktails. How much should Gino charge the hosts of this party?

example

Work out 73.6 ÷ 8 using
a repeated subtraction   **b** short division.

· ·

a 73.6
   72.0
   ────   8 × ⑨ = 72
    1.6
    1.6
   ────   8 × (0.2) = 1.6
     0

73.6 ÷ 8 = 9 + 0.2 = 9.2

b   9.2
      8)73.¹6

1 Use the method of repeated subtraction to calculate these.
All the answers are whole numbers.
   a 216 ÷ 4   **b** 272 ÷ 8   **c** 322 ÷ 7   **d** 231 ÷ 11   **e** 555 ÷ 15

2 Calculate these using an appropriate method. Give each answer
with a remainder.
   a 249 ÷ 8   **b** 209 ÷ 9   **c** 596 ÷ 14   **d** 2864 ÷ 23   **e** 4206 ÷ 41

3 Calculate these. Give each answer as a decimal.
   a 9.36 ÷ 3   **b** 19.28 ÷ 4   **c** 59.28 ÷ 8   **d** 37.05 ÷ 5
   e 3.672 ÷ 6   **f** 19.26 ÷ 9   **g** 166.95 ÷ 7   **h** 289.52 ÷ 8

4 Calculate these. You will need to add extra zeros to help
you complete the division. Give each answer as a decimal.
   a 25.8 ÷ 5   **b** 52 ÷ 8   **c** 6.75 ÷ 6   **d** 9.3 ÷ 4   **e** 41.4 ÷ 8

5 a Philip is allocating tutors for a training session at his
company. Each tutor should have at most 15 employees
in his group. 252 employees work for Philip's company.
How many tutors does Philip need?
   b Gemma shares a lottery win of £6093.45 between herself and
14 members of her family. How much does each person receive?
   c Lily and her seven friends share the cost of a restaurant meal
equally between themselves. If the total bill is £129.20, how
much do they each pay?

7f Calculator methods

A school bus can seat 48 students. 222 students use these buses to travel to the theatre. How many buses are needed? Are all the buses full and if not, how many students are on the bus that is not full?

$222 \div 48 = 4.625$

5 buses are required but one is not full. On this bus there are $0.625 \times 48 = 30$ students.

1 Calculate these. Where appropriate, give your answer to 2dp.

a $1.3^2 - 0.75$ **b** $2.9 \times \sqrt{29.16}$ **c** $(8.94 - 3.04)^2$

d $18.9 - (3.4 + 0.68)^2$ **e** $\dfrac{4.1 + 8.75}{\sqrt{16}}$ **f** $\dfrac{(3.05 - 1.63)^2}{5}$

g $\dfrac{8.23 + 4.6}{\sqrt{1.5 + 0.95}}$ **h** $\left(\dfrac{4.8}{3.6}\right)^2$

2 Use a calculator to work these out. For each answer turn your calculator display upside down and write the word that is shown on the display. Write the sentence that all six words make.

a $18^2 + 7 \times 3$ **b** $135 + (205 + 35)^2$

c $25^2 - \sqrt{49}$ **d** $22^2 \times 10 - 22 \times 10 - 6$

e $\sqrt{0.09} + \dfrac{0.3667}{5}$ **f** $145 + \left(\dfrac{575}{2.5}\right)^2$

3 Use a calculator to solve these problems. Give your answers in a form appropriate to the question.

a Chocolate eggs are packed in boxes of 48. How many boxes are needed to pack 1400 eggs and how many eggs are left over?

b A box of 48 eggs costs £18.00. How much does each egg cost?

c Five school friends share a box of 48 chocolate eggs. How many eggs do they each receive and how many eggs are left?

d Neil eats three of his eggs in 4 minutes and 15 seconds. How long does he take to eat each egg?

Write the reading on this scale.

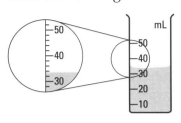

The level of the liquid in this measuring cylinder is between 30 and 40 ml. There are 5 divisions between 30 and 40 ml so each division is 10 ÷ 5 = 2 ml.
The reading is 34 ml of liquid.

1 Match the objects on the left with an appropriate measurement from the table on the right.

Length of pencil
Length of a book
Height of door
Capacity of a cup

2 m
17 cm
250 ml
25 cm

2 Write the readings on these scales.

a

b

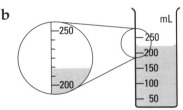

3 Estimate the readings on these scales.

a

b

example

Find the area of this rectangle in

a cm²   **b** mm²

1.5 cm

8 mm

. . . .

a 8 mm ÷ 10 = 0.8 cm   Convert mm to cm
   1.5 cm × 0.8 cm = 1.2 cm²   Then use area = length × width
b 1.2 cm² = 1.2 × 100   Convert cm² to mm²
         = 120 mm²

1 Convert these metric measurements to the units indicated
in brackets.

a 12 m (cm)   **b** 24 cm (mm)
c 75 cl (ml)   **d** 4.5 litres (ml)
e 1.25 kg (g)   **f** 0.55 tonnes (kg)
g 5 m² (cm²)   **h** 6.5 ha (m²)

2 Convert these metric measurements to the units indicated
in brackets.

a 430 cm (m)   **b** 75 mm (cm)
c 75 cl (litres)   **d** 2750 ml (litres)
e 815 g (kg)   **f** 9045 kg (tonnes)
g 43 500 cm² (m²)   **h** 125 000 m² (ha)

3 Convert these imperial units to their rough metric equivalents.

a 21 feet (m)   **b** 64 inches (cm)
c 12 gallons (litres)   **d** 110 pounds (kg)

4 Convert these measurements of time to the units indicated in brackets.

a 12 minutes (seconds)   **b** 7 days (hours)
c 220 minutes (hours)   **d** 200 hours (days)

5 a A shortbread biscuit weighs 30 g. The biscuits are sold in packs
of 8. What is the mass of a pack of biscuits in **i** grams **ii** kg?
b The distance between Clutton and Tattenhall is 5.8 km. What is
this distance in **i** metres? **ii** millimetres?

example

> P(X) = 0.4. Work out P(not X).
> ....
> P(not X) = 1 − P(X)
>   = 1 − 0.4
>   = 0.6

1

Copy this probability scale and place these cards at the correct points on the scale.

| Evens | | Unlikely | | Certain | | Impossible | | Likely |

2 Show the likelihood of each of these events happening on a probability scale.

  a If you toss a coin you will get a 'head'.
  b If you throw a dice you will get a six.
  c Tomorrow will be Tuesday.
  d It will snow tomorrow.
  e London will host the 2012 Olympics.
  f When you next write your first name, you will write the letter 'a'.
  g Your maths teacher will win the National Lottery this week.
  h Your head teacher will grant your maths class an extra week's summer holiday for exceptional work.

3

| P(A) = 0.7 | | P(B) = 0 | | P(C) = 0.5 | | P(D) = 0.2 |

  a Draw a probability scale and mark these events on it.
  b What is the probability that event A does not happen?
  c Write P(not D).
  d Describe P(B) in words.
  e Give an example of an event that has the same probability as event C.

example

Four discs numbered 2, 4, 6 and 8 are placed in a bag. Charlie chooses a disc at random. What is the probability that he chooses

a a 6　**b** an even number　**c** a number more than 4?

....

a $P(6) = \frac{1}{4}$　　　　There is one 6 amongst four numbers.
b $P(\text{an even number}) = \frac{4}{4} = 1$　All four numbers are even numbers.

1 You spin this spinner once.
  a List all the possible outcomes.
  b Are all the outcomes equally likely? Explain your answer.
  c Write
    i P(the spinner lands on red)
    ii P(the spinner lands on blue).

2 You throw a fair dice.
  a List all the possible outcomes.
  b Are all the outcomes equally likely? Explain your answer.
  c Write
    i P(the dice lands on 3)
    ii P(the dice lands on an even number).

3 A tin contains 10 metallic crayons. Five crayons are gold, three crayons are silver and two crayons are bronze. Freya chooses a crayon at random. What is the probability that the crayon is
  a silver　　　**b** gold　　　**c** not bronze　　　**d** pewter?

4 Eight balls numbered 1 to 8 are placed in a hat. Amber selects a ball at random. What is the probability that she selects
  a a 4　　　　　　　　**b** an odd number
  c a number less than 7　**d** a rabbit?

example

John throws an ordinary dice.

a Are the events 'John throws a 6' and 'John throws an odd number' mutually exclusive?

b What is the probability that John throws a 6 or an odd number?

. . . .

a Yes, because these events cannot occur together. A 6 is not odd.

b P(6 or an odd number) $= $ P(6) + P(odd number)
$$= \frac{1}{6} + \frac{3}{6} = \frac{4}{6} = \frac{2}{3}$$

1 When a coin is tossed the events 'toss a head' and 'toss a tail' are mutually exclusive. True or false?

2 Jack is playing with his trolley of bricks. The bricks are numbered 1, 2, 3, 4 and 5. The table gives the probability that Jack selects a brick painted with a particular number. What is the probability that Jack selects a brick

	P(1) = 0.3
	P(2) = 0.1
	P(3) = 0.25
	P(4) = 0.15
	P(5) =

a numbered 5

b numbered 3 or 4

c numbered 1, 2 or 3?

3 A multi-pack bag of crisps contains 8 packets. Three of the packets are flavoured with sea salt, three with balsamic vinegar and the rest with cracked black pepper. Ashim chooses a packet of crisps at random.

a Are the events 'choose a packet flavoured with sea salt', 'choose a packet flavoured with balsamic vinegar' and 'choose a packet flavoured with cracked black pepper' mutually exclusive?

b What is the probability that Ashim chooses a packet flavoured with cracked black pepper or a packet flavoured with sea salt?

Paula tosses a coin 100 times and obtains these results.

| Head | 45 times |
| Tail | 55 times |

a Estimate the probability that on the next toss, Paula will get

  i a head   **ii** a tail.

b How could Paula improve her probability estimates?

· ·

a i $P(\text{Head}) = \frac{45}{100} = \frac{9}{20}$ **ii** $P(\text{Tail}) = \frac{55}{100} = \frac{11}{20}$

b She should toss the coin more times – the more trials conducted, the better the probability estimate.

1 Jason has a bag of discs. He selects one disc at a time without looking, records the symbol on the disc and then replaces the disc in the bag. Here are his results.

Symbol	Star	Circle	Heart	Question mark

a Work out the number of times Jason selected a disc.

b Jason selects another disc. Estimate the probability of selecting

  i a circle   **ii** a question mark   **iii** a star or a heart.

c The bag only contains discs which are printed with one of four symbols. These are stars, circles, hearts and question marks. True or false? Explain your answer.

2 Luke has a pencil case containing blue and black pens. He chooses a pen at random, records its colour and replaces the pen in his case. Here are his results.

| Blue | 20 times |
| Black | 10 times |

a Estimate the probability that the next pen Luke selects is   **i** blue   **ii** black.

b Luke actually has 6 pens in his case. Estimate how many of each colour he has.

example

A dice in the shape of a tetrahedron has faces numbered from 1 to 4. The dice is thrown 100 times. How many times would you expect to see **a** a 1 **b** an odd number?

a $P(1) = \frac{1}{4}$ and $\frac{1}{4} \times 100 = 25$ times

b $P(\text{an odd number}) = \frac{2}{4} = \frac{1}{2}$ and $\frac{1}{2} \times 100 = 50$ times.

1 A dice is thrown 120 times.

  a How many times would you expect to see

  i a 6   **ii** a 1 or a 2   **iii** an even number?

  Here are the results of these 120 throws.

Score	1	2	3	4	5	6
Frequency	18	15	45	14	20	8

  b Is the dice biased? Explain your answer.

2 A dice is biased so that the probability of throwing a 6 is 0.35.

  a After 100 throws of the dice, how many sixes would you expect?

  b After 500 throws of the dice, how many sixes would you expect?

3 Simon, Robbie and Flip all test the same 10p coin for bias. These are their results.

Simon		Robbie		Flip	
20 tosses		50 tosses		200 tosses	
H	T	H	T	H	T
15	5	32	18	112	88

  a Giving your answer as a decimal, estimate the probability of tossing a head using the results table for **i** Simon **ii** Robbie **iii** Flip.

  b What conclusion would you draw from each person's data?

  c Which conclusion is likely to be the most reliable? Why?

  d What should Simon, Robbie and Flip do with their data to reach an even more reliable conclusion?

9a Properties of triangles

Identify the two ways in which
this triangle can be classified.

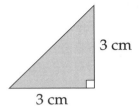

3 cm

3 cm

. . . .

The triangle has two equal sides and one right angle.
This triangle is right-angled and isosceles.

1 Copy and complete this table about triangles.

Name of triangle	Number of equal sides	Number of equal angles	Number of right angles
Isosceles			0 or 1
	3		
Right-angled	0 or 2		

2 State whether each of these triangles is equilateral, isosceles,
scalene or right-angled. Explain your answers.

a

b

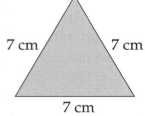

7 cm   7 cm

7 cm

c

23 mm   45 mm

48 mm

d

29°

61°

example

> Sketch and name all the
> quadrilaterals with two different
> pairs of equal and opposite
> angles.
>
>
>
> Parallelogram   Rhombus

1 Match these shapes with their descriptions and name
each shape.

a Four equal sides, opposite sides are parallel,
opposite angles are equal, diagonals bisect at 90°
and are different lengths.
b Opposite sides are parallel and equal in length,
four 90° angles, diagonals bisect each other and
are equal in length.
c Opposite sides are parallel and equal in length,
opposite angles are equal, diagonals bisect each
other and are different lengths.
d One pair of opposite and parallel sides.

2

| Square | Kite | Trapezium |

| Rectangle | Rhombus | Parallelogram |

From the choices above, choose all the quadrilaterals that have
a four equal angles
b one pair of equal and opposite angles
c both diagonals bisected by each other
d diagonals that bisect at 90°.

Sketch two different ways in which a triangular prism can be cut to leave two identical prisms. Describe the resulting prisms.

Equilateral triangle

Equilateral triangle

Two triangular prisms with the same cross-section as the original.

Two triangular prisms with a right-angled triangle cross-section.

1 Describe two different ways in which each of these prisms can be cut in order to leave two identical prisms. Sketch your answers.

    a cuboid   **b** cylinder.

2 a Use the formula $v + f - e = 2$ where $v =$ vertices, $f =$ faces and $e =$ edges, to copy and complete this table.

Name of solid	Number of vertices, v	Number of faces, f	Number of edges, e
tetrahedron	4	4	
cube	8		12
octahedron	6	8	
dodecahedron		12	30

    b Can you find out the collective name of these five solids?

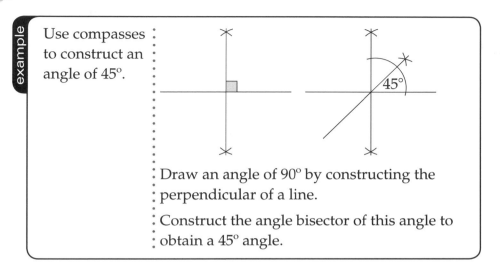

Use compasses to construct an angle of 45°.

Draw an angle of 90° by constructing the perpendicular of a line.

Construct the angle bisector of this angle to obtain a 45° angle.

1 a Draw a line *XY*, so that *XY* = 5.6 cm.
b Using compasses, construct the perpendicular bisector of *XY* and label it *AB*. Label the midpoint of *XY* as *M*.
c Measure the length of *XM*. Check that it is the same as the length *MY*.
d Construct the bisector of angle *AMY*.

2 Use compasses to construct an angle of $22\frac{1}{2}°$. $\boxed{22\frac{1}{2}° \text{ is half of } 45°.}$

3 a Draw a line *AC*, so that *AC* = 4 cm.
b Using compasses, construct the perpendicular bisector of *AC* and label the points where the arcs meet *B* and *D* (with *D* below *B*).
c Join the points in alphabetical order (*A* to *B*, *B* to *C* etc.).
d Name the quadrilateral that you have constructed.

example

From a point, X, on the ground, the angle of elevation of the top of a building is 40°. X is 12 m away from the base of the building. Find the height of the building.

Not to scale

Building

Make an accurate drawing where 1 cm represents 1 m.

By measuring you can see that the height of the building is 10 m.

1 Construct these triangles (ASA).

a

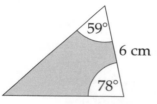

59°

6 cm

78°

b 4 cm

63°

40°

2 Construct these triangles (SAS).
State the type of each triangle.

a

4.5 cm

55°

5 cm

b

3 cm

75°

5.8 cm

3 From a point, X, on the ground, the angle of elevation of the top of a tree is 34°.
X is 7.5 m away from the base of the tree.
By making an accurate drawing where 1 cm on the diagram represents 1 m in real life, work out the height of the tree.

Tre

X 34°

7.5 m

example

Write 484 as a product of its prime factors and use this to explain why 484 is a square number.

$484 = 2 \times 242 = 2 \times 2 \times 121 = 2 \times 2 \times 11 \times 11 = 2^2 \times 11^2$

484 can be written as $(2 \times 11) \times (2 \times 11)$, a number multiplied by itself, which is the definition of a square number.

1 Without using a calculator, write the value of these.

    a 7^2 **b** 15^2 **c** $\sqrt{49}$ **d** $\sqrt{81}$ **e** $\sqrt{196}$

2 Use your calculator to find each of these.

    a 27^2 **b** 9.8^2 **c** $\sqrt{1156}$ **d** $\sqrt{2704}$ **d** $\sqrt{153.76}$

3 a Copy and continue this sequence for three more lines.

$$1 = 1$$
$$1 + 3 = 4$$
$$1 + 3 + 5 = 9$$

  b What type of numbers are on the right-hand side of each equation?

4 a Between which two whole numbers does $\sqrt{253}$ lie?

  b Use your calculator to find a good estimate for $\sqrt{253}$.

5 a Write 324 as a product of its prime factors and use this to explain why 324 is a square number.

  b Without using a calculator find $\sqrt{324}$.

6 a Write 48 as a product of its prime factors.

  b Use part **a** to help you find the smallest number that 48 can be multiplied by to give a square number.

example

Work out each of these.

a 4^3 **b** -2^5 **c** 10^4

....

a $4^3 = 4 \times 4 \times 4 = 64$

b $-2^5 = -2 \times -2 \times -2 \times -2 \times -2 = -32$

c $10^4 = 10 \times 10 \times 10 \times 10 = 10\,000$

1 Without using a calculator, write the value of these.

   a 3^3 **b** 5^3 **c** 3^4 **d** $\sqrt[3]{8}$ **e** $\sqrt[3]{64}$

2 Use your calculator to find each of these.

   a 8^3 **b** 4.5^3 **c** -2^3 **d** $\sqrt[3]{3375}$ **e** $\sqrt[3]{-64}$

3 a Copy and complete this sequence for three more lines.

$$1^3 = 1^2$$
$$1^3 + 2^3 = 3^2$$
$$1^3 + 2^3 + 3^3 = 6^2$$
$$1^3 + 2^3 + 3^3 + 4^3 = 10^2$$

   b What is the name of the sequence that begins 1, 3, 6, 10, …?

4 There are two numbers between 1 and 100 that are both a square number and a cube number. One of them is 1. What is the other?

5 Use your calculator to find each of these.

   a 2^5 **b** 6^3 **c** 3^4 **d** 10^6 **e** 25^5

example

Find the LCM of 6 and 14.

List some multiples of 6: 6, 12, 18, 24, 30, 36, (42), 48, …
List some multiples of 14: 14, 28, (42), 56, 70, …
Choose the smallest number that appears in both lists.
The LCM of 6 and 14 is 42.

1 Write the first eight multiples of these numbers.

  a 3   **b** 5   **c** 8   **d** 12   **e** 25

2 Using your answers to question **1** to help you, find the lowest common multiple (LCM) of these pairs of numbers.

  a 3 and 5   **b** 3 and 8   **c** 8 and 12   **d** 5 and 25

3 This table shows all the products that make up the numbers 12 and 15. Copy and complete the table and find the highest common factor (HCF) of 12 and 15.

Number	Products			Factors
12	1 × 12	2 × 6	3 × 4	
15	1 × 15	3 × 5		

4 Find the HCF of these pairs of numbers.

  a 8 and 10   **b** 6 and 15   **c** 18 and 30   **d** 7 and 29

  e What can you say about the numbers in part **d**?

5 True or false? Explain your answers.

  a The smallest factor of any number is 1.

  b All numbers except 1 have an even number of factors.

  c Any multiple of 8 is also a multiple of 2 and 4.

example

Tilly writes 120 as $p^3 \times q \times r$ where p, q and r are prime.
Find the values of p, q and r.

So $120 = 2^3 \times 3 \times 5$

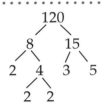

1 Copy and complete this prime factor decomposition of 24.

    $24 = 2 \times \square \times \square \times \square$

2 Write each number as a product of its prime factors.

    a 16   **b** 36   **c** 60   **d** 126   **e** 180

3 Clara writes the prime factor decomposition of a
number as $2^3 \times 5^2 \times 11$.
What number is she working with?

4 The prime factor decomposition of 392 is $2^3 \times 7^2$.
Use this fact to work out if

    a 6 is a factor of 392.
    b 14 is a factor of 392.

5 108 can be written as $x^2 \times y^3$ where x and y are prime.
Find the values of x and y.

> **example**
>
> Three vertices of an isosceles trapezium are A (-1, 2), B (2, 2) and C (3, 0). Plot a fourth point, D, to complete the quadrilateral.
> **a** Write the coordinates of point D.
> **b** Find which two angles are equal.
>
>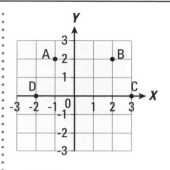
>
> **a** (-2, 0)
> **b** The two equal angles are ADC and BCD.

1 Draw a set of axes with values from -3 to 3.
  a Plot and join the points (1, 3), (3, 0), (1, -3), (-1, 0) and (1, 3).
  b Name the quadrilateral that you have drawn.
  c Write the coordinates of the intersection of the diagonals.

2 Draw a set of axes with values from -5 to 5.
  a Plot the points (2, 0), (-1, -2) and (-4, 0) and do not join them.
  b If you joined the points, what type of triangle would you have drawn?
  c Plot a fourth point to create a rhombus. What are the coordinates of this point?

3 Draw a set of axes with values from -3 to 3.
  a Plot the points (-1, 2) and (3, 2) and join them with a straight line. Write the coordinates of the midpoint of this line.
  b Plot the points (-2, -3) and (-2, 2) and join them with a straight line. Write the coordinates of the midpoint of this line.
  c Write a method to find the coordinates of the midpoint of a line. Use your method to find the coordinates of the midpoint of the line joining the points (-5, 7) and (1, -5).

example

Write two lines that intersect at the point (-1, 4).

A line that passes through (-1, 4) is the straight line made up of points whose x coordinates are all -1. For example, (-1, 0), (-1, 1), (-1, 2), (-1, 3), (-1, 4). This is the line $x = -1$.

Another line that passes through (-1, 4) is the straight line made up of points whose y coordinates are all 4. For example,

1 Draw a set of axes with values from -5 to 5 and plot these graphs.

   a $x = 3$ **b** $y = 2$ **c** $x = -4$ **d** $y = -1$ **e** $x = 0$

2 a Write the coordinates of the point where the lines $x = -1$ and $y = 2$ intersect.

   b Write what you notice about the value of the x coordinate and the value of the y coordinate when you compare these coordinates with the equations of the lines.

   c The point of intersection of these two lines is the top left-hand corner of a square of area 9 units². Write the equations of the two lines needed to complete this square.

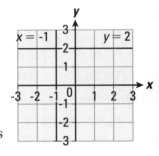

3 Without drawing the graphs, write where these lines intersect.

   a $x = 3$ and $y = 1$ **b** $x = 2$ and $y = -3$ **c** $x = -5$ and $y = -4$

4 Write two lines that intersect at these points.

example

Generate the three coordinates that lie on the graph of $y = 3x + 1$.

Substitute $x = 1$ $y = (3 \times 1) + 1 = 4$

Substitute $x = 2$ $y = (3 \times 2) + 1 = 7$

Substitute $x = 3$ $y = (3 \times 3) + 1 = 10$

The coordinates are $(1, 4)$, $(2, 7)$ and $(3, 10)$.

1 a Copy and complete these tables to generate three
coordinates for each of these line graphs.

  i $y = 3x + 2$

x	1	2	3

  ii $x + y = 4$

x	1	2	3
y			

  b Draw each graph on a separate set of axes.

2 a For each linear function, copy and complete the coordinates.

  i $y = 2x + 3$ $(-2, \square)$ $(\square, 3)$ $(2, \square)$

  ii $y = -x$ $(-3, \square)$ $(\square, -1)$ $(2, \square)$

  b Plot the graphs of $y = 2x + 3$ and $y = -x$ on the same axes.

  c Write the coordinates of the point where these two lines intersect.

3 Matt and Damon are builders. Matt charges a fee of £80 plus £30
for each hour that he works. Damon charges a fee of £100 plus
£20 for each hour that he works.

  a Draw a set of axes with x values from 0 to 8 (representing
the number of hours worked) and y values from 0 to
320 in steps of 20 (representing the total cost of the job).

  b Plot a line graph for each builder.

  c Which builder would you use for the job if the time taken was

    i 1 hour   **ii** 2 hours   **iii** 6 hours?

example

For this table of x and y coordinates write the equation of the line on

| x | 1 | 2 | 3 | 4 | 5 |

....

which these points lie.

The y coordinates go up in fours so this is based on the four times table. The y coordinate is three less than four times the

1 a For each set of coordinates use the 'help-line' to spot a pattern and write this pattern in words.

Coordinates	'Help-line'
i (4, 1), (4, 2), (4, 3)	Look at the x values.
ii (1, 4), (2, 3), (3, 2)	Add the x and y values.

b Write each of your patterns in words as an equation.

2 For each table write the equation of the line on which the points lie.

a

x	1	2	3	4	5
y	-3	-3	-3	-3	-3

b

x	1	2	3	4	5
y	5	4	3	2	1

3 a Write five coordinates that lie on this graph.

b Find a pattern between these coordinates and use this to write the equation of this line.

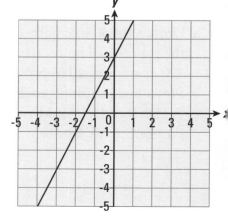

example

Harry the cat has 24 pouches of food. 9 of these pouches are tuna and the rest are chicken. What proportion of the pouches are chicken? Give your answer as

a a fraction **b** a percentage.

. . . .

$24 - 9 = 15$ so 15 of the pouches are chicken.

The proportion that are chicken is

a $\dfrac{15}{24} = \dfrac{5}{8}$ (÷3)

b $(5 \div 8) \times 100\% = 62.5\%$

1 Write each of these fractions as hundredths. Then convert each fraction to **i** a decimal **ii** a percentage.

a $\dfrac{3}{4}$ **b** $\dfrac{2}{5}$ **c** $\dfrac{11}{20}$ **d** $\dfrac{26}{25}$

2 Use a calculator to change each of these fractions to **i** a decimal **ii** a percentage.

a $\dfrac{1}{8}$ **b** $\dfrac{19}{40}$ **c** $\dfrac{8}{9}$ **d** $\dfrac{17}{32}$

3 Michael has a haulage business with 16 lorries. Five of his lorries are white and all the rest are blue. Six of his lorries are in need of repair.

a Write the proportion of lorries that are in need of repair as
   i a fraction in its simplest form **ii** a percentage.
b What proportion of Michael's lorries are blue?

4 Lynda has a library of books. $\dfrac{3}{4}$ of her books are novels and $\dfrac{3}{16}$ of her books are reference books. The rest of her books are on the subject of Italy.

a If Lynda has 200 books, how many are novels?
b What proportion of Lynda's books are on the subject of Italy?

example

8 jam tarts cost £1.20. Work out the cost of 20 jam tarts.
. . . .
The cost of 1 jam tart is £1.20 ÷ 8 = £0.15

1 Copy and complete this table to work out the cost of 5 metres of fabric if 12 metres of fabric costs £546.

Amount of fabric in metres	Cost in £

2 40 litres of diesel costs £38.20. Work out the cost of
   a 1 litre of diesel   **b** 5 litres of diesel
   c 18 litres of diesel   **d** 45 litres of diesel

3 This is a recipe for making 8 scones.
   Write out a recipe for making
   12 scones.

200 g	self-raising flour
50 g	soft margarine
25 g	sugar
50 g	currants
1	egg

4 Nappies come in two pack sizes.
   a Is the amount of nappies in a pack in direct proportion with the cost?
   b Which pack is better value for money? Show your working.

Cost £5.92

Cost £8.96

In 1982, the ratio of sheep to people in New Zealand was 20 : 1.
If there were 70.3 million sheep, how large was the population?
. . . .
70.3 million is 20 parts.
1 part is 70.3 million ÷ 20 = 3.515 million.
The population was approximately 3.5 million people.

1 Write each of these ratios in its simplest form.

   a 2 : 10   **b** 12 : 8

   c 15 : 25   **d** 6 : 2 : 10

   e £18 : £6   **f** 6 kg : 15 kg

   g 250 g : 5 kg   **h** 24p : £1.80

   i 2.5 hours : 100 minutes **j** 56 cm : 2.8 m : 140 mm

2 In a class of 24 students there are 18 boys.

   a Write the ratio of boys to girls in its simplest form.

   b Write the ratio of girls to boys in its simplest form.

3 The ratio of Dora's pocket money to Diego's pocket money is 4 : 5.

   a If Dora receives £4.80 per week, work out how much pocket
      money Diego receives.

   b Dora has her weekly pocket money increased by 45p. Work out
      the new ratio of Dora's pocket money to Diego's pocket money.

4 A map has a scale of 1 : 20 000.

   a What is the distance in real life of a measurement of 8 cm on the
      map? Give your answer in kilometres.

   b What is the measurement on the map of a distance of 300 m in
      real life? Give your answer in centimetres.

5 The angles in a triangle are in the ratio 2 : 2 : 5.

   a Work out the sizes of the angles of the triangle.

   b What type of triangle is this?

example

James is making a glass of his favourite cordial. The bottle suggests using water and cordial in the ratio 1 : 4. James's glass has a capacity of 250 ml. How much water should he pour into his glass?

Divide 250 ml into 1 + 4 = 5 equal parts.
1 part is 250 ml ÷ 5 = 50 ml.

1 Divide each of these quantities in the ratio given in brackets.

  a £20 (1 : 4)   **b** 50 cm (3 : 7)

  c 55 kg (3 : 8)   **d** 108 litres (3 : 4 : 5)

2 An alloy is a mixture of two elements, at least one of which is a metal.

  a Bronze is made from combining copper and tin in the ratio 22 : 3. Calculate, in kilograms, the mass of copper and tin in a bronze statue of mass 100 kg.

  b Brass is made from combining copper and zinc in the ratio 9 : 1. Calculate, in grams, the mass of copper and zinc in a brass sundial of mass 4 kg.

3 In the United Kingdom, silver-coloured coins are made from cupro-nickel, an alloy of copper and nickel. In cupro-nickel, the ratio of copper to nickel is 3 : 1.

  a A 50p coin has a mass of 8 g. Calculate the mass of copper and nickel in a 50p coin.

  b A 10p coin has a mass of 6.5 g. Calculate the mass of copper and nickel in a 10p coin.

4 Annabelle is making a fruity drink. She uses apple juice, ginger ale and lemonade in the ratio 4 : 2 : 1. Annabelle's glass has a capacity of 280 ml.

Work out the amount of each ingredient that she needs.

> **example**
>
> Angus and Hamish share £40 in the ratio 3 : 5. Write the proportion of money that Hamish receives and use this to calculate the amount.
> . . . .
> There are $3 + 5 = 8$ parts and so Hamish receives $\frac{5}{8}$ of the money.
> $\frac{5}{8}$ of £40 $= \frac{1}{8} \times 5 \times 40 = \frac{200}{8} =$ £25. So Hamish receives £25.

1 In a class of 25 students, 3 are left-handed.
  a Write the ratio of left-handed students to right-handed students.
  b Write the proportion of students that are left-handed.
  c The proportion of left-handed students in this class is the same as in the UK population. If the UK population is approximately 60 million people, estimate the number of left-handed people.

2 Jack makes a 5 litre tin of pale pink paint by mixing 3.5 litres of brilliant white paint with 1.5 litres of ruby red paint.
  a Write the ratio of ruby red to brilliant white paint.
  b Write the proportion of the paint that is ruby red.

3 To make chocolate buttercream for a batch of fairy cakes, Florence mixes together 180 g of icing sugar, 120 g of butter and 60 g of cocoa powder.
  a Write the ratio of icing sugar to butter to cocoa powder.
  b What proportion of the buttercream is cocoa powder?
  c Scale up this recipe to make 480 g of buttercream.

4 In the UK there are currently some 2 million North American grey squirrels and only 160 000 native red squirrels.
  a Write the ratio of grey to red squirrels in its simplest form.
  b What proportion of the UK squirrel population is red?
  c Of the red squirrels, $\frac{3}{16}$ live in England. Write the ratio of red squirrels in England to red squirrels in the rest of the UK.

12a Further substitution

a Write an expression for the perimeter of this rectangle.

$y + 3$

x

b Simplify the expression by collecting like terms.

c Find the perimeter of the rectangle if $x = 5$ and $y = -1$.

a $x + x + y + 3 + y + 3$

b $2x + 2y + 6$

c $(2 \times 5) + (2 \times -1) + 6 = 10 - 2 + 6$
$$= 14 \text{ units}$$

1 If $w = 5$, $x = 2$ and $y = -3$, find the value of each expression.

a $y + 5$	**b** $x - 9$	**c** $3w$	**d** x^2
e $2x + w$	**f** $3y + 5x$	**g** xy	**h** $wx + 4$
i $2w^2$	**j** y^3	**k** $xy + w$	**l** $10 - wx$

2 Simplify these expressions by collecting like terms. Then find the value of each expression given that $a = -3$ and $b = 2$.

a $5b + 2b$ **b** $2a + 6b - a$ **c** $4b - 3a + b - 5$

d $2ab + 3ba$ **e** $2a^2 + 5a + b + a$ **f** $b^2 + 7b^2 + 10a$

3 a Write an expression for the area of this rectangle.

4

$n - 3$

b Simplify your expression expanding any brackets.

c Given that $n = 8$, work out the area of this rectangle.

4 Match the pairs of cards with equivalent expressions. Show your work.

$4x - 8$	$2(2x - 1)$	$4x - 2$	$4x^2 - x$
$x(4x - 1)$	$4(x - 2)$	$4x - 6$	$2(2x - 3)$

Simplify these expressions. **a** $3x \times 4$ **b** $3p \times 5q$ **c** $2a \times 6a$

a $3x \times 4 = 3 \times 4 \times x$
        $= 12x$
b $3p \times 5q = 3 \times 5 \times p \times q$
            $= 15pq$
c $2a \times 6a = 2 \times 6 \times a \times a$
            $= 12a^2$

1 Simplify these expressions as fully as possible.

  a $a \times 3$ **b** $6p \times 2$ **c** $k \times 4k$ **d** $3p \times q$

  e $2m \times 5n$ **f** $4a \times 3b \times 2c$ **g** $2w \times 8xy$ **h** $5g \times 3g^2$

2 Expand and simplify these expressions.

  a $5(a + 3)$ **b** $4(x - 1)$

  c $10(2 - p)$ **d** $x(y + 3)$

  e $2(k + 3) + 4(k + 1)$ **f** $7(t + 2) - 4(t + 1)$

  g $a(a + 5) + a(a - 2)$ **h** $3p(5p - 2)$

  i $5x(3x + 2y)$ **j** $2a(3a + 4) + 6a(2a + 1)$

3 Write a simplified expression for the area of
  this rectangle.

4 a Write a simplified expression for the area of
    this square.

  b If $x = 3$, find the area of this square.

example

Simplify

a $\dfrac{15ab}{3b}$

b $\dfrac{a^2 + 4a}{a}$

. . . .

a $\dfrac{15ab}{3b} = \dfrac{\cancel{15} \times a \times \cancel{b}}{\cancel{3} \times \cancel{b}} = 5a$

b a is a factor of both a^2 and $4a$ and so it can be cancelled.

1 Simplify these expressions as fully as possible.

a $x \div 5$ **b** $2 \div y$ **c** $8m \div 2$ **d** $5k \div 10$

e $\dfrac{12a}{4}$ **f** $\dfrac{21b}{7b}$ **g** $\dfrac{3xy}{9x}$ **h** $\dfrac{24t^2}{3t}$

2 Mark Kim's homework. If you find a mistake then please correct it for her, explaining where she went wrong.

a $\dfrac{5x}{5} = x$ **b** $\dfrac{k + 7}{7} = k$ **c** $\dfrac{3d^2}{d} = 3d$

d $\dfrac{2ab^2}{4b} = 2ab$ **e** $\dfrac{10t + 18}{5} = 2t + 18$

3 Simplify these expressions.

a $\dfrac{10x + 4}{2}$ **b** $\dfrac{4a - 12}{4}$ **c** $\dfrac{10p - 15q}{5}$

d $\dfrac{18m + 12n}{6}$ **e** $\dfrac{x^2 + 3x}{x}$ **f** $\dfrac{5a + a^2}{a}$

g $\dfrac{b^2 - 7b}{b}$ **h** $\dfrac{8t - 4t^2}{2t}$ **i** $\dfrac{12f + 6f^2}{3f}$

example

Solve   **a** $5(x + 3) = 10$ **b** $\dfrac{k}{5} + 3 = 10$

a $5(x + 3) = 10$

$5x + 15 = 10$ Multiply brackets.

$5x = -5$ Subtract 15.

$x = -1$ Divide by 5.

b $\dfrac{k}{5} = 7$ Subtract 3.

$k = 35$ Multiply by 5.

1 Solve these equations.

  a $x + 3 = 8$ **b** $a - 5 = 9$

  c $12 + p = 25$ **d** $17 = t - 14$

  e $8k = 24$ **f** $12x = 0$

  g $\dfrac{a}{9} = 7$ **h** $1 = \dfrac{b}{6}$

2 Solve these equations.

  a $4x + 5 = 17$ **b** $9g - 2 = 16$

  c $18 + 2a = 28$ **d** $\dfrac{k}{3} + 7 = 10$

  e $4(d + 7) = 32$ **f** $3(t - 9) = 18$

  g $2x^2 = 32$ **h** $\dfrac{b^3}{4} = 16$

3 Solve these equations. You should find each answer on one of these number cards.

 4   -16 $2\frac{1}{2}$ 0 $\frac{1}{4}$ 27 -1 5

  a $3m + 5 = 20$ **b** $2(x + 5) = 8$

  c $\frac{1}{4}p = 1$ **d** $6 = 6 + 3k$

  e $\dfrac{t}{9} - 3 = 0$ **f** $4a - 1 = 9$

  g $4(q + 3) = 13$ **h** $\dfrac{d}{8} + 4 = 2$

12d Unknowns on both sides

example

Solve this equation.

$9(x + 2) = 5(x + 4)$

$9x + 18 = 5x + 20$ Expand the brackets

$4x + 18 = 20$ Subtract $5x$ from both sides

$4x = 2$ Subtract 18 from both sides

1 Solve these equations.

a $4x = 3x + 10$ **b** $12p = 8p + 16$

c $10k = 4k - 6$ **d** $3t + 15 = 13t$

e $2(n + 5) = 6n$ **f** $6y - 18 = 3y$

g $8(w - 6) = 2w$ **h** $7(a + 3) = 4a$

2 Pierre is solving an equation with unknowns on both sides.
Unfortunately, he has muddled up his lines of working.
Can you help him?

$8n = 16$ $8n - 6 = 10$

$n = 2$ $12n - 6 = 4n + 10$

3 Solve these equations.

a $5n + 7 = 3n + 11$ **b** $4p + 8 = 10p + 2$

c $4x + 7 = x + 16$ **d** $3y - 4 = 2y + 3$

e $8k + 10 = 13k - 5$ **f** $12t - 1 = 14t - 5$

4 Solve these equations.

a $4(x + 2) = 3x + 11$ **b** $9p + 6 = 3(p + 8)$

c $5(t - 2) = t + 10$ **d** $7y - 9 = 3(y + 5)$

e $4(k + 2) = 3(k + 5)$ **f** $3(n + 4) = 5(n + 1)$

g $12(b - 3) = 8(b - 2)$ **h** $6(a + 3) = 4(a - 1)$

13a Reflection

a Draw a set of axes with *x* values from -5 to 5 and *y* values from 0 to 5. Plot the points (0, 0), (0, 3), (3, 3) and (5, 0).
b Reflect this shape in the *y*-axis and name the resulting shape.
c List the coordinates of the four vertices of the resulting shape.

· ·

b The shape is an isosceles trapezium.
c The vertices are (-5, 0), (-3, 3), (3, 3) and (5, 0).

1 Copy each diagram and reflect each shape in the mirror line.

a   **b**   **c**

2 Copy this diagram.
  a Reflect the shape in line 1.
  b Reflect both the original shape and image from part **a** in line 2.

Line 2

Line 1

3 Draw a set of axes with *x* and *y* values from -5 to 5.
  a Plot and join the points (1, 1), (2, 3), (5, 3) and (4, 1).
  b Name the shape that you have drawn and label it P.
  c Reflect this shape in the *x*-axis and label its image A.
  d Write the coordinates of shape A.
  e Reflect shape P in the *y*-axis and label its image B.
  f Write the coordinates of shape B.

Shape Reflection   75

13b Rotation

example

a Plot and join the coordinates (1, 0), (1, 3), (2, 3), (2, 1), (3, 1) and (3, 0).
Label this shape L_1.

b Rotate L_1 through 90° anticlockwise about (0, -1) and label the image L_2.

a, b

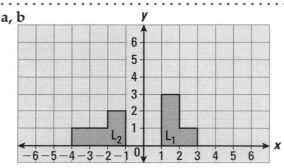

1 Copy and rotate each shape through the given angle where C is the centre of rotation.

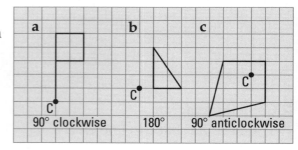

a	b	c
90° clockwise	180°	90° anticlockwise

2 Draw a set of axes with x values from -6 to 6 and y values from 0 to 6.

a Plot and join the coordinates (2, 2), (4, 2) and (2, 5). Label this triangle T_1.

b Rotate triangle T_1 through 90° clockwise about (2, 2) and label the image T_2.

c Rotate triangle T_2 through 180° about (0, 2) and label the image T_3.

d Describe the rotation that will take triangle T_1 directly to triangle

example

Copy and complete this shape so that it has rotation symmetry of order 4 about the centre, C.

You need to rotate the shape 90° clockwise, 180° and 90° anticlockwise.

1 a Copy these road signs and draw the lines of symmetry, if possible.

  b For each road sign, state the order of rotation symmetry.

2 a Copy these shapes and draw the lines of symmetry, if possible.

  b For each shape, state the order of rotation symmetry.

Isosceles
triangle

Parallelogram

Regular
pentagon

Regular
hexagon

3 a Copy this diagram. Using the centre of rotation, C, complete the shape so that it has rotation symmetry of order 2.

  b Copy the diagram again. Using the centre of rotation, C, complete the shape so that it has rotation symmetry of order 4.

13d Translation

example

a Translate rectangle A 4 units to the right and 3 units down.

b Describe the translation that returns rectangle A to its original position.

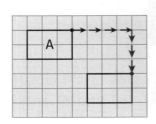

a Note how the top right-hand vertex is still the top right-hand vertex after the translation.

1 When a triangle is translated, point A on the triangle translates to point B on the image.

a Describe the translation of point A to point B.

b Copy the triangle and complete the image.

2 Describe these translations.

a A to B	**b** B to A	**c** B to D
d C to E	**e** E to B	**f** A to E
g D to C	**h** C to A	

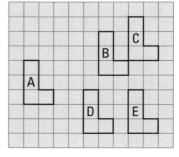

3 Draw a set of axes with values from -8 to 8.

a Plot and join the coordinates (1, 1), (2, 4), (3, 4) and (2, 1).

b Name this shape and label it P.

c For each of the points in part **a**, add 2 to the *x*-coordinate and subtract 3 from the *y*-coordinate. Write the new coordinates.

d Plot and join these new coordinates and label the shape Q.

e Describe the translation of shape P to shape Q.

13e Enlargement

example

Triangle T_2 is an enlargement of triangle T_1. Calculate the scale factor.
. . . .
All lengths on triangle T_2 are twice those on T_1. The scale factor is 2.

1 a Which of these shapes are enlargements of triangle T?

  b Write the scale factor of each enlargement.

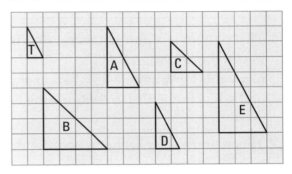

2 a Which of these shapes are enlargements of rectangle R?

  b Write the scale factor of each enlargement.

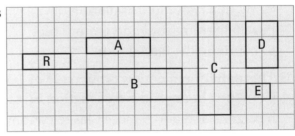

3 Copy and enlarge these shapes by the scale factor given.

  a Scale factor 2
  b Scale factor 4
  c Scale factor 2
  d Scale factor 3

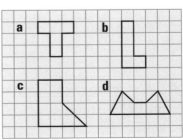

Tessellate this shape
six times.

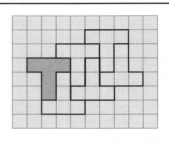

1 This pattern is a parquet wood flooring in a
herringbone design.
Copy this herringbone tessellation of rectangles
and add 6 more tiles to continue the tessellation.

2 This pattern is a parquet wood flooring in
a chevron design.
Copy this chevron tessellation of
parallelograms and add 6 more tiles
to continue the tessellation.

3 This pattern is a honeycomb made by bees.
Copy this honeycomb tessellation of
hexagons and add 6 more tiles to continue
the tessellation.

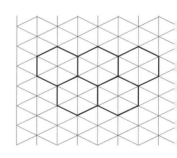

4 Copy these tessellations using pentominoes
and add 6 more tiles to continue the pattern.

14a Planning a statistical enquiry

example

A village community plans to install a children's playground. A committee has to decide on the type of play equipment and should consider its safety.

What **a** primary data **b** secondary data could the committee collect?

. . . .

a The committee could ask the parents in the village what sort of equipment they would prefer, taking into consideration its safety.

b The committee could research accident statistics for different types of play equipment and use these to aid their decision.

1 Decide whether primary or secondary data has been collected as a result of these enquiries.

a A High Street bank decides to update the graphics on its most popular credit card. The bank asks members of the public to select their favourite credit card from a set of six photographs.

b A chocolate manufacturer wants to make sure that each milk chocolate bar that it produces has a mass of at least 100 g. Every tenth bar is removed from the production line and weighed.

c A school situated on a A-road wants to persuade its local council to install a speed camera outside the main gates. The school produces a report using accident statistics from the past 5 years.

2 Write whether you would collect primary or secondary data for these statistical enquiries. Explain your answer.

a Deciding whether or not your school has a good attendance record.

b Deciding whether or not to change the colour of your school uniform to pink.

c Deciding whether or not to introduce a basket-weaving class as a lunchtime activity at your school.

14b Collecting data

Mrs Hinds wants to know whether the students in her school believe they are getting the right amount of homework each night. Design a data collection sheet for Mrs Hinds to use.

Amount of homework				
Name	Too little	Just right	Too much	Not sure

1 Mark wants to plant a hedge. He decides to investigate different varieties and base his decision on how tall the hedge will grow and whether or not it is evergreen.
Design a data record sheet for Mark to use.

2 Nicky is buying a new Ford Focus car. She wants to draw up a data collection sheet on which she can record the features that are important to her. These are the size of the engine, the fuel type, the transmission (manual or automatic) and whether or not the car has a full service history.
 a Design a data record sheet on which Nicky can record the cars she has seen.
 b Suggest two other features that she may like to add to her data record sheet.

3 Lauren wants to know how different students travel to school and whether age makes a difference to their choice of transport.
Design a data collection sheet for her to use.

4 Callum is planning to organise a trip to a leisure centre for all his friends. He decides to find out the available facilities at all his local centres in order to decide the best one to go to.
Create a data record sheet for Callum to use.

example

Write what is wrong with this question and suggest improvements.

> Which is your favourite flavour of crisps?
> ☐ Cheese and onion   ☐ Prawn cocktail

....

This question will leave some people feeling that they were unable to give their opinion. More categories should be added.

> ☐ Salt and vinegar   ☐ Ready salted
> ☐ Beef   ☐ Other

1 For each survey, write why the place chosen for conducting the survey may bias the results.

 a To find out the popularity of school dinners by asking students as they leave the school canteen.

 b To find out the preferred type of music by asking members of the public as they leave a Kylie Minogue concert.

 c To find out the preferred brand of toilet paper by asking all the people leaving a superstore at 2 p.m. on a Monday.

2 Rupert writes this survey to find out opinions on films.

> 1. Don't you think that comedy is the best type of film?
>
> 2. How often do you buy films on DVD?
> ☐ A lot   ☐ A little
>
> 3. How old are you?
> ☐ 10 and under   ☐ 10–40   ☐ Over 50

 a Write what is wrong with each of these questions.

 b Improve and rewrite each question.

 c Add another question of your own that would improve this survey.

example

This is a grouped frequency table showing the rainfall, r, in millimetres during June from 1998 to 2007.

Rainfall, r, in mm	Frequency
$0 \leq r < 30$	3
$30 \leq r < 60$	9
$60 \leq r < 90$	3
$90 \leq r < 120$	2
$120 \leq r < 150$	2
$150 \leq r < 180$	1

a What does the group $150 \leq r < 180$ mean?

b State the modal class.

....

a This means that the rainfall is more than or equal to 150 mm and less than 180 mm.

1 These are the heights, h, in cm of a group of 30 Year 7 girls.

145.4	147.0	142.3	150.6	148.5	152.5	141.0	149.3	152.6
147.8	143.3	142.4	154.9	150.8	151.4	139.2	146.7	138.5
145.6	144.7	146.9	148.8	150.6	153.0	146.2	144.1	147.0
158.3	149.8	143.9						

a Copy and complete this grouped frequency table.

Height, h, in metres	Tally	Frequency
$135 \leq h < 140$		
$140 \leq h < 145$		
$145 \leq h < 150$		
$150 \leq h < 155$		
$155 \leq h < 160$		

b State the modal class.

c This group of Year 7 girls are going on a trip to Alton Towers. They are all keen to ride 'Oblivion' but the height restriction says you must be over 1.4 m.

The table shows information about the mean temperature recorded in England each October between 1977 and 2006.

Mean temperature, $t\,°C$	$6 \leq t < 8$	$8 \leq t < 10$	$10 \leq t < 12$	$12 \leq t < 14$
Frequency	1	5	20	4

Draw a pie chart to represent this information.

· ·

The total frequency $= 1 + 5 + 20 + 4$

$\qquad\qquad\qquad\quad = 30$

Each temperature $= \dfrac{360°}{30} = 12°$

The sectors are

$1 \times 12° = 12°$

$5 \times 12° = 60°$

$20 \times 12° = 240°$

$4 \times 12° = 48°$

1 A class votes for their favourite from four series of children's books. The table shows their choices.

Series of books	Votes	Angle
Harry Potter	8	$8 \times \square° = \square°$
His Dark Materials	10	$10 \times \square° = \square°$
A Series of Unfortunate Events	5	
The Chronicles of Narnia	7	

a Calculate the angle of the pie chart for each vote.

b Copy and complete the table.

c Draw a pie chart to show the results of the vote.

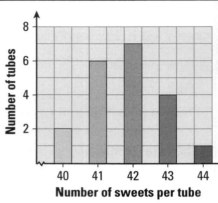

example

Isla opened 20 tubes of 'Sweeties' and counted the number of sweets inside. These are her results as a frequency diagram.

Find   **a** the range
       b the mode
       c the median
       d the mean
number of sweets per tube.

....

a $44 - 40 = 4$

b 42 sweets. This is the highest bar on the graph.

c 42 sweets. There are 20 tubes so the median lies between the 10th and 11th value, or in the bar for 42 sweets.

d Mean $= \dfrac{(2 \times 40) + (6 \times 41) + (7 \times 42) + (4 \times 43) + (1 \times 44)}{20} = 41.8$ sweets

1 This graph shows how children travelled to school in Great Britain in 2005.

a In 2005, what was the most common way to get to school for children aged 11 to 16?

b What percentage of 5- to 10-year-olds walked to school in 2005?

Between 1995 and 1997, 38% of 5- to 10-year-olds travelled to school by car.

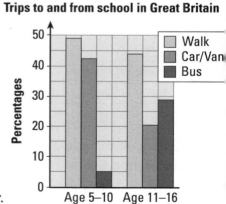

c Write the percentage increase or decrease of the popularity of travelling to school by car.

d Can you think of a reason why this has happened?

example

This graph shows information about TV viewing habits in 2002.

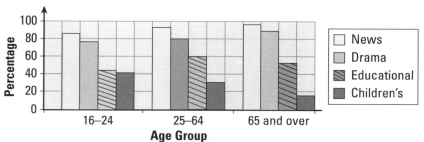

a Which age group watches the most 'Educational' TV?

b Which is the most popular type of TV programme?

c Write a sentence to compare the TV viewing habits of young and elderly people.

· ·

a 25–64 year olds **b** News programmes

c Elderly people watch more News, Drama and Educational programmes than young people, but much less Children's.

1 This graph shows information on the proportion of households that had access to certain types of home entertainment in 1998/9 and 2002/3.

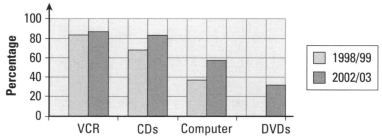

a In 2002/3, what percentage of homes had access to a computer?

b What was the increase in the percentage of households that had access to CDs between 1998/9 and 2002/3?

c Why do you think that there is no bar for DVDs in 1998/9?

d Describe what the bar for 'VCR' will look like in 2006/7.

This table gives information about the 200 m running times, in seconds, for two 13-year-old athletes.

	Mean	Range
Tristan	24.79	2.14

Compare Tristan's and Simon's performances.
. . . .
Tristan has the lowest mean time so he is, on average, the faster athlete. However, Simon has a smaller range, so he is more consistent.

1 Twins Alex and Imogen are arguing over their examination results. Each twin believes that they have achieved the most noteworthy scores. Here are their percentages.

	Maths	English	Science	Spanish	History	Art
Alex	73	84	54	65	94	50

   a Calculate **i** the mean **ii** the range for each set of results.
   b Compare the twins' results using your calculations from part **a**.

2 Julia and Ryan wait tables in a restaurant. At the end of each night the amount that they have made in tips gives a basic indication of the quality of service that they have given. Here are their tips for one week.

Julia	£28	£16	£43	£12	£35	£30	£11

   a Calculate the **i** mean **ii** median **iii** mode **iv** range for each person's data.
   b A promotion is available for one person. Which average would you use to demonstrate the quality of service that you give if you were **i** Julia **ii** Ryan?

example

Only one of these numbers is a prime number.

| 151 | | 153 |

a Which is which?

b List the factors of each number.

· ·

a If a number is divisible by 3 then the sum of its digits is divisible by 3.

For 153, $1 + 5 + 3 = 9$ and so 3 is a factor of 153.

A prime number has only 1 and itself as factors so 151 must be prime.

b The factors of 151 are 1 and 151.

The factors of 153 are 1, 3, 9, 17, 51 and 153.

1 Write all the factors of

  a 12   **b** 21   **c** 24   **d** 30   **e** 55

2 a Write the factors of

  i 4   **ii** 16   **iii** 25   **iv** 49   **v** 81

  b The numbers in part **a** are square numbers. What do you notice about the number of factors of square numbers? Explain why.

3 A number is divisible by 9 if the sum of the digits is divisible by 9. Is 9 is a factor of these numbers?

  a 108   **b** 280   **c** 567   **d** 2549   **e** 8478

4 A number is divisible by 6 if it is an even number and the sum of its digits is divisible by 3. Is 6 a factor of these numbers?

  a 145   **b** 234   **c** 321   **d** 982   **e** 2412

5 Use divisibility tests to find out which of these numbers are prime.

  a 31   **b** 47   **c** 51   **d** 63   **e** 89

15b LCM and HCF

example

Given that $132 = 2 \times 2 \times 3 \times 11$ and $252 = 2 \times 2 \times 3 \times 3 \times 7$ find
a the HCF of 132 and 252
b the LCM of 132 and 252.

. . . .

a $132 = ②×②×③×11$
$252 = ②×②×③× 3 \times 7$

Choose the prime factors that 132 and 252 have in common and multiply these together. $2 \times 2 \times 3 = 12$

b $132 = ②²× 3 \times 11$
$252 = 2^2 × ③² × ⑦ × ⑪$

Choose the highest power of each prime factor in the two lists and multiply these together. $2^2 \times 3^2 \times 7 \times 11 = 2772$

1 From this box of numbers write

| 4 | 7 | 17 | 21 | 23 | 25 |

   a two multiples of 7   **b** two factors of 28
   c two square numbers   **d** two prime numbers.

2 a List the first five multiples of 3.
  b List the first five multiples of 5.
  c Use your lists to write the LCM of 3 and 5.

3 Find the LCM of
   a 4 and 6   **b** 8 and 10   **c** 9 and 15   **d** 2, 4 and 5

4 a List the factors of 12.
  b List the factors of 30.
  c Use your lists to write all the common factors of 12 and 30.
  d Write the HCF of 12 and 30.

5 Find the HCF of
   a 6 and 10   **b** 12 and 24   **c** 24 and 32   **d** 12, 15 and 45

6 Given that $126 = 2 \times 3 \times 3 \times 7$ and $396 = 2 \times 2 \times 3 \times 3 \times 11$
  find   **a** the HCF of 126 and 396   **b** the LCM of 126 and 396.

example

Use the method of partitioning to work out
a 12×3.9 **b** $675 \div 9$
. . . .
a $12 \times 3.9 = 10 \times 3.9 + 2 \times 3.9 = 39 + 7.8 = 46.8$
b $675 \div 9 = 630 \div 9 + 45 \div 9 = 70 + 5 = 75$

1 Recall and use the methods of using factors, partitioning, compensation and doubling and halving to work these out mentally.
a 12×50 **b** 7.5×400 **c** 11×6.4 **d** $336 \div 8$
e 45×19 **f** 23×21 **g** 12×4.5 **h** 3.8×5

2 You can think of multiplying by 0.1 and 0.01 as dividing by 10 and 100. Similarly, dividing by 0.1 and 0.01 can be thought of as multiplying by 10 and 100. Use these facts to calculate these questions mentally.
a 14×0.1 **b** 560×0.01 **c** $1.6 \div 0.01$ **d** 250×0.1
e $8.9 \div 0.1$ **f** $0.63 \div 0.01$ **g** 75×0.01 **h** $0.09 \div 0.1$

3 Without a calculator, calculate
a 12^2 **b** 4^3 **c** 2^4 **d** 1^3
e $2^2 + 5^2$ **f** $(2 + 5)^2$ **g** $7^2 - 3^2$ **h** $(7 - 3)^2$

4 Without a calculator, calculate
a $\sqrt{25}$ **b** $\sqrt{169}$ **c** $\sqrt[3]{8}$ **d** $\sqrt[3]{64}$
e $\sqrt{9} + \sqrt{16}$ **f** $\sqrt{9 + 16}$ **g** $\sqrt{100} - \sqrt{64}$ **h** $\sqrt{100 - 64}$

5 a Work these out mentally
  i $2^2 \times 3^2$ **ii** $(2 \times 3)^2$
  b Write what you notice.

6 a Work these out mentally
  i $\sqrt{25} \times \sqrt{4}$ **ii** $\sqrt{25 \times 4}$
  b Write what you notice.

example

Calculate 21.4×9.8 using the grid method.

First estimate the answer. 21.4×9.8 $20 \times 10 = 200$

Change the calculation to an equivalent whole number calculation. $21.4 \times 9.8 = 214 \times 98 \div 100$

×	200	10	4
90	$200 \times 90 = 18\,000$	$10 \times 90 = 900$	$4 \times 90 = 360$
8	$200 \times 8 = 1600$	$10 \times 8 = 80$	$4 \times 8 = 32$

$18\,000 + 1600 + 900 + 360 + 80 + 32 = 20\,972$

1 a Copy and complete this estimate.

629×18 $600 \times \square = \square$

b Copy and complete this grid to calculate 629×18.

×	600	20	9
10	$600 \times 10 = 6000$		
8			

2 Calculate

a 26.1×5	**b** 42.8×9	**c** 52.5×6	**d** 8×71.4
e 4.38×4	**f** 6.35×7	**g** 5×8.49	**h** 9×5.98

3 Calculate

a 1.22×14	**b** 2.34×21	**c** 33×5.09	**d** 8.35×52
e 27.5×3.4	**f** 4.5×4.86	**g** 5.19×7.3	**h** 9.2×84.7

4 a Shamoon tops up the tank of his car with 45 litres of diesel at a cost of 97.4p per litre. Work out the total cost of the diesel.

b Aysha buys 7.4 metres of voile at £8.95 per metre. Work out the total cost of the voile.

example

Calculate 67.7 ÷ 15 giving your answer to 2 decimal places.

Estimating the answer gives $67.7 \div 15 \approx 70 \div 20 = 3.5$

$$\begin{array}{r} 4.\ 5\ 1\ 3 \\ 15\overline{)67.^77^20^50} \end{array}$$

Work out the answer to 3 decimal places in order to round to 2 decimal places. So 67.7 ÷ 15 = 4.51 (2dp)

1 Calculate these using an appropriate method. The whole number answers can all be found in the box.

33	29	48	57	41	52	31	86

a 246 ÷ 6   **b** 416 ÷ 8   **c** 774 ÷ 9

d 336 ÷ 7   **e** 434 ÷ 14   **f** 348 ÷ 12

g 924 ÷ 28   **h** 1368 ÷ 24

2 Calculate these. Where appropriate, give your answer as a decimal to 1 decimal place.

a 128 ÷ 6   **b** 194 ÷ 9   **c** 164 ÷ 7

d 233 ÷ 11   **e** 97.7 ÷ 15   **f** 86.9 ÷ 17

g 80.8 ÷ 18   **h** 95.6 ÷ 19

3 a A 750 ml bottle of Softy fabric conditioner claims to last for 21 washes. How much Softy should be used for one wash? Give your answer to 2 decimal places.

b Softy fabric conditioner costs £1.38.
How much does each wash cost to the nearest penny?

c Comfy fabric conditioner is sold in 500 ml bottles for the same price. One 30 ml capful of Comfy should be used per wash. Which fabric conditioner is the best value for money?

15f Calculator methods

Flora was born 239 days ago.

Calculate how old Flora is in weeks and days.

. . . .

Divide by 7 (7 days in a week) $239 \div 7 = 34.142\ 857\ 14\ldots$

Convert the remainder $0.142\ 857\ 14\ldots \times 7 = 1$
by multiplying by the divisor.

So Flora is 34 weeks and 1 day old.

1 Work out the age of these babies in weeks and days.

   a Holly   96 days   **b** Lily   153 days   **c** Annabelle   304 days

2 Convert these measurements of time to the units given in brackets.

   a 3.4 hours (hours and minutes) **b** 136 minutes (hours and minutes)

   c 2.125 days (days and hours)   **d** 525 hours (days and hours)

   e 6.3 minutes (mins and secs)   **f** 3280 seconds (mins and secs)

   g 11.8 years (years and days)   **h** 4500 days (years and days)

3 Give your answers to these questions in a form appropriate to the situation.

   a Xavier is flying to Switzerland to sell ski-goggles. One boxed pair of goggles has a mass of 300 g. Xavier must not exceed his baggage allowance of 23 kg. How many pairs of goggles can he take and how much baggage allowance is left over?

   b Xavier buys each pair of ski-goggles for €188.50 and plans to sell them for €220. If he sells 45 pairs on his trip, how much profit will he make?

example

Calculate $2\frac{3}{5}$ of 10 kg.

$2\frac{3}{5}$ of 10 kg $= \frac{13}{1\cancel{5}} \times \cancel{10}^{2}$

$\qquad = \frac{13}{1} \times 2 = 26$ kg

1 Change these improper fractions into whole or mixed numbers.

   a $\frac{10}{3}$ **b** $\frac{9}{5}$ **c** $\frac{22}{7}$ **d** $\frac{51}{17}$ **e** $\frac{27}{12}$

2 Change these mixed numbers into improper fractions.

   a $2\frac{1}{3}$ **b** $4\frac{1}{2}$ **c** $1\frac{4}{7}$ **d** $5\frac{5}{6}$ **e** $7\frac{4}{9}$

3 Work out these, giving your answers as mixed numbers.

   a $\frac{2}{3}$ of 4 cm   **b** $\frac{4}{5} \times 6$ **c** $\frac{5}{9}$ of 7 kg   **d** $4 \times \frac{11}{20}$

   e $\frac{17}{24} \times 16$ **f** $24 \times \frac{11}{30}$ **g** $1\frac{1}{8}$ of 20 litres   **h** $2\frac{2}{9}$ of 12 m

4 Write the number of

   a halves in 10   **b** thirds in 5

   c quarters in 3   **d** fifths in 2

5 Calculate

   a $4 \div \frac{1}{7}$ **b** $5 \div \frac{1}{9}$ **c** $7 \div \frac{2}{3}$ **d** $9 \div \frac{3}{5}$ **e** $12 \div \frac{8}{9}$

6 a Leaf fills plant pots with compost from a 30 litre bag.

    Each plant pot will hold $\frac{3}{4}$ litre of compost.

    How many pots can he fill?

   b David makes plant labels by cutting $8\frac{1}{2}$ cm lengths

    from a plank of wood 153 cm long.

    How many labels can he cut?

example

A pair of designer sunglasses costs £135. In an end-of-season sale the sunglasses are reduced by 5%. Work out the cost of the sunglasses in the sale.

$(100 - 5)\%$ of the old price $= 95\%$ of £135

1 Work out each answer and then write the letter that is in that position in the alphabet. For example, if your answer is 8 write h as h is in the 8th position in the alphabet. Find the hidden word.

a 20% of 95   **b** $17\frac{1}{2}\%$ of 120   **c** 8% of 200   **d** 12.5% of 40

e 45% of 40   **f** 1% of 200   **g** $33\frac{1}{3}\%$ of 36   **h** 4% of 625

2 Copy and complete.

a An increase of 5% is the same as multiplying by 1.0☐

b An increase of 25% is the same as multiplying by 1.☐☐

c A decrease of 8% is the same as multiplying by 0.9☐

d A decrease of 12% is the same as multiplying by 0.☐☐

3 Calculate these percentage changes.

a Increase £15 by 10%   **b** Increase 24 m by 25%

c Decrease 50 kg by 12%   **d** Increase 19 litres by 6%

e Decrease £35 by 24%   **f** Decrease 750 cl by 16%

g Increase 45 g by 74%   **h** Decrease 108 cm by 70%

4 a A 500 ml bottle of surface cleaner is advertised with an additional 20% extra free. How much surface cleaner does the promotional bottle contain?

b House prices in the North West increased by 12% from 2005 to 2006. In 2005 the average house price was £138 000. Calculate the average house price in 2006.

c A car bought for £14 300 in 2005 depreciates by 22% in the first year. What is this car worth in 2006?

16a Further equations

example

Solve $4(x - 5) = 8 - 3x$.

$4x - 20 = 8 - 3x$	Expand the brackets
$7x - 20 = 8$	Add $3x$ to both sides
$7x = 28$	Add 20 to both sides
$x = 4$	Divide both sides by 7

1 Show that all these equations have a solution of $x = 3$.

  a $x + 9 = 12$ **b** $4x - 7 = 5$

  c $5(x - 1) = 10$ **d** $\frac{x}{3} + 5 = 6$

  e $7x = 2x + 15$ **f** $6(x - 2) = 2x$

  g $8x - 10 = 3x + 5$ **h** $4(x + 2) = 5(x + 1)$

2 Joe is solving an equation. Unfortunately, he has muddled up his lines of working.

Can you unscramble them for him?

$t = 2$ $7t - 3 = 11$ $5t - 3 = 11 - 2t$ $7t = 14$

3 Solve these equations.

  a $5t - 6 = 8 - 2t$ **b** $10 - 3y = 2y - 5$

  c $3(n - 9) = 13 - 5n$ **d** $7 - 4a = 5(a - 4)$

  e $2(p - 4) = 4(1 - p)$ **f** $6(k - 3) = 4(3 - k)$

4 Write an equation to describe each problem and then solve your equation to answer the problem.

  a I think of a number, double it and subtract 7. I get the same answer as when I subtract the number from 11. Find the number.

  b I think of a number, multiply it by 3 and subtract 8. I get the same answer as when I multiply the number by 2 and subtract it from 12. Find the number.

16b Constructing equations

The sum of three consecutive even numbers is 108. Find these numbers.

....

If the first number is x, the next two even numbers are $x + 2$ and $x + 4$

$$x + (x + 2) + (x + 4) = 108$$
$$3x + 6 = 108$$
$$3x = 102$$
$$x = 34$$

1 The sum of Talitha's current age and her age 5 years ago is the same as her age in 3 years' time.

   a Let Talitha's current age be x. Write an expression in terms of x for her age 5 years ago.

   b Write an expression in terms of x for her age in 3 years' time.

   c Construct an equation in x and solve it to find Talitha's age.

2 The sum of three consecutive whole numbers is 57.

   a Let the first number be x. Write an expression in terms of x for the next two consecutive numbers.

   b Construct an equation in x and solve it to find these numbers.

3 This rectangle has an area of 20 units². Write an equation to find x.

$3x - 2$

5

4 Three friends spend £500 on a shopping trip. Keira spends three times as much as Aimée who spends £100 more than Suzanne. Work out how much each friend spends.

example

The equation of a graph is given by the formula $y = 3x + 2$.
Rebecca knows that the point (✸, 8) lies on the graph but she
has smudged the ink on the x-coordinate. Find the missing
x-coordinate.

8 is the y-coordinate so $8 = 3x + 2$

$6 = 3x$ Subtract 2

$2 = x$ Divide by 3

So the point is $(2, 8)$

1 A formula for the perimeter of this rectangle
is $P = 2(a + b)$.

a Find the perimeter, P, if the length $a = 17$ cm
and the width $b = 12$ cm.

b Find P if $a = 14$ m and $b = 8$ m.

c Find b given that $P = 30$ mm and $a = 9$ mm.

2 To convert temperatures from degrees Celsius (°C) to
degrees Fahrenheit (°F) you use this formula.

$$C = 5\left(\frac{F - 32}{9}\right)$$

Copy and complete this table of average temperatures
on some planets in our solar system.

	Venus	Earth	Mars	Saturn	Pluto
°C	464		-65	-140	
°F		59			-373

3 This formula converts British pounds (P) to euros (E).

$$E = 0.67P$$

a Convert £200 to euros.

b Convert €217.75 to pounds.

c Write a formula for converting euros to British pounds.

16d Further sequences

Find the position-to-term rule for the sequence 19, 18, 17, 16, 15, …

Position	1	2	3	4	5
Multiply by -1	-1	-2	-3	-4	-5
Add 20	20	20	20	20	20

The position-to-term rule is $T(n) = -n + 20 = 20 - n$

1 Copy and complete this pattern in order to find the first three terms of the sequence given by the position-to-term rule $T(n) = 2n + 5$.

$$T(1) = 2 \times 1 + 5 = \square$$
$$T(2) = 2 \times \square + 5 = \square$$
$$T(3) = 2 \times \square + \square = \square$$

2 Generate the first five terms of the sequences described by these rules.

    a $T(n) = 4n$ **b** $T(n) = 2n + 1$

    c $T(n) = 5n - 3$ **d** $T(n) = 10 - n$

3 For each sequence in question **2** find $T(100)$.

4 Copy and complete this table to find the position-to-term rule for the sequence 1, 5, 9, 13, 17, …

Position	1	2	3	4	5
Multiply by $\square$	4	8	12		
Add $\square$					

Write the rule in algebra.

5 Find, in algebra, the position-to-term rule for these linear sequences.

    a 3, 6, 9, 12, 15, …   **b** 5, 7, 9, 11, 13, …

    c 7, 10, 13, 16, 19, …   **d** 14, 13, 12, 11, 10, …

example

Look at the structure of these diagrams and generate a formula for the sequence.

Diagram 1   Diagram 2   Diagram 3

In each pattern, *s* squares are made using 3*s* straws plus one straw to close the final square.
The formula is $n = 3s + 1$ where *n* is the number of straws.

1 Look at the structure of the diagrams in this sequence and explain why the formula works.

  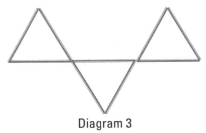

Diagram 1   Diagram 2   Diagram 3

$s = 3t$ where *s* = the number of straws
                  and   *t* = the number of triangles.

2 Look at the structure of the diagrams in this sequence and generate a formula to connect the given variables.

Diagram 1   Diagram 2   Diagram 3

s = the number of straws
h = the number of hexagons.

example

Generate two points on the graph of $x - 3y = 6$.

We can let $x = 0$ and $y = 0$, in turn, to generate two points.

When $y = 0$, $x = 6$ When $x = 0$, $-3y = 6$

                            Dividing by $-3y = -2$

1 Match these graphs with their equations.

$y = 2$ $y = -3$ $y = x + 1$

$x = 0$ $x = 2$ $y = x + 3$

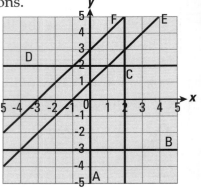

2 a Copy and complete these tables to generate three coordinate pairs for each line graph.

  i $y = 2x + 2$

x	1	2	3

  ii $y = x + 3$

x	1	2	3

  b Draw the graphs above on the same set of axes.

  c Write the point of intersection of the two graphs.

3 a For each equation copy and complete this table of values.

x	0	

  i $x + y = 5$ **ii** $x + 2y = 6$ **iii** $2x + 3y = 6$

  b Draw a set of axes with values from -8 to 8 and plot these three graphs.

16g Real-life graphs

Describe Sarah's car journey shown by this distance–time graph.

Sarah sets off and drives for 30 km during the first half an hour. She is therefore driving at an average speed of 60 km per hour.

She stops for 15 minutes and then drives for another 15 minutes, covering a distance of 10 km. She is now driving at an average speed of 40 km per hour. Her journey finishes 40 km away from her starting point.

1 Aura shows this distance–time graph to her friend Moggie and explains that it shows her journey to her Grandmother's house. Moggie immediately tells Aura that this is impossible. How does Moggie know?

2 Plot a graph of 'Distance from home' against 'Time' for this journey.

Jamie leaves his house at 7 a.m. for work. He walks 6 km in one hour and then stops at a café. He takes half an hour to eat his breakfast and then walks the last 2 km to work, arriving at 9 a.m. He spends 15 minutes trying to get in to his building before realising it is Sunday. At this point Jamie borrows an onlooker's bicycle and cycles home in half an hour.

a What time did Jamie arrive back home?
b At what speed did he cycle on his return journey?

3 £10 is currently worth 18 New Zealand dollars. Construct a conversion graph to convert British pounds to New Zealand dollars and vice versa. Go up to £50. Use your graph to convert
a £25 to New Zealand dollars.   **b** $27 to British pounds.

Write the usual names of
a a regular triangle
b a regular quadrilateral.
. . . .
a A triangle with equal sides and equal angles is an equilateral triangle.

1 a Write the names of these regular polygons.

i ii iii

  b Write the number of lines of symmetry of each shape.
  c Write the order of rotation symmetry of each shape.

2 This pentagon has been divided into three triangles by drawing the diagonals from one vertex.

Copy and complete.
  a The sum of the interior angles of a pentagon is $3 \times 180° = \square°$
  b One interior angle of a pentagon is $\square° \div 5 = \square°$
  c Use this method to work out the interior angle of a hexagon.

Construct a triangle with sides of length 3.5 cm, 3.5 cm and 5 cm.
Not to scale

A   B   A   B   A   B

Draw a straight
line of 5 cm.

Draw an arc at A
with compasses set
at 3.5 cm.

Draw an arc at B
with compasses set
at 3.5 cm.

1 a Using compasses and a protractor, construct these triangles.

i

x

70° 7.7 cm 45°

ii

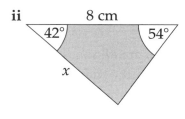

8 cm

42° 54°

x

b Use your ruler to measure the lines marked x.

2 a Using only compasses, construct triangles with sides of length
   i 3 cm, 4 cm and 5 cm
   ii 2 cm, 5 cm and 5 cm
   iii 4 cm, 4 cm and 4 cm
  b Write the mathematical name of each triangle in part **a**.

3   William says   Matilda replies

No you haven't!

I have drawn a triangle
with sides of length
3 cm, 4 cm, 7 cm.

Matilda has not looked at William's book.
How can she be so sure?

These are the plan, front elevation and side elevation for a solid.
Draw the solid.

Plan   Front elevation   Side elevation

1 These solids are all made out of five centimetre cubes. For each
solid draw   **i** the plan   **ii** the front elevation
(from the direction of the arrow). Use square grid paper.

a   **b**   **c**

2 These are the plan, front elevation and side elevation for
a solid. Draw the solid.

Plan   Front elevation   Side elevation

Calculate **a** the volume **b** the surface area of a 3 cm by 6 cm by 7 cm cuboid.

a Volume of a cuboid = length × width × height
$$= 3 \times 6 \times 7$$
$$= 126 \text{ cm}^3$$

b Surface area = $(2 \times 3 \times 6) + (2 \times 3 \times 7) + (2 \times 6 \times 7)$
$$= 162 \text{ cm}^2$$

1 Which of these nets will fold to form a cube?

a
b
c
d

2 a Calculate the volume of this cuboid.
  b Calculate the surface area of this cuboid.
  c Draw a net of this cuboid.

4 cm

3 cm

6 cm

3 Which of these cubes could be formed from this net?

a
b

c
d

> Draw the locus of all points that are 1 cm away from a straight line AB of length 5 cm. Describe the locus in words.
>
>
> Not actual size
>
> The locus is two lines parallel to and the same length as AB, joined at either end with semicircles whose centres are A and B.

1 Draw a sketch and describe in words the locus of
   a the tip of the minute hand on a clock as the time changes from 2 o'clock to 3 o'clock
   b the tip of the hour hand on a clock as the time changes from 2 o'clock to 3 o'clock
   c the top right-hand corner of a page of this book if you turn that page over
   d the centre of a car wheel as the car travels along a road
   e a point on the tyre of a car as the car travels along a road.
   Hint: For part **e,** mark a point on a coin and roll it along your ruler.

2 For these questions, the locus of the point will involve shading a region. Draw a sketch and describe in words the locus of
   a a garden sprinkler with a reach of 4 m
   b a dog tethered to a fence by a lead of length 3 m.

3 a Draw two points, X and Y, 6 cm apart. Draw the locus of all points equidistant from X and Y.
   Hint: Pick a few points where the distance to X is the same as the distance to Y and mark with dots. These dots should help you draw this locus.
   b On the same diagram, draw the locus of all points that are 2 cm away from Y.
   Hint: 'Plot' a few points that are 2 cm from Y. You should begin to

> A scale model of an Aston Martin Vanquish S car has length
> 14.6 cm and width 6 cm. The scale used to build the model is
> 1 : 32 which means that for every 1 cm on the model, the real
> Aston Martin uses 32 cm. Calculate, in mm, the real dimensions
> of an Aston Martin Vanquish S.
> ....
> 14.6 cm × 32 = 467.2 cm   6 × 32 = 192 cm
> To convert cm to mm × 10.
> The dimensions of the real car are 4672 mm by 1920 mm.

1 This is a scale drawing of
Carlos's bedroom. The scale is
1 cm represents 50 cm.

  a Measure the length and
  width of Carlos's bedroom
  on the plan.
  b Write the actual length and
  width of Carlos's bedroom.
  c What is the width of Carlos's
  desk?
  d Carlos wants to hang fairy lights across one of the diagonals
  of his room. What is the minimum length of fairy lights that
  he requires?

2 A scale model of a Jaguar XK8 car is 20.0 cm long.
The scale used to build the model is 1 : 24 which means that for
every 1 cm on the model, the real Jaguar uses 24 cm.
  a Work out the actual length of a Jaguar XK8.
  b The actual width of a Jaguar XK8 is 2071 mm. Work out how
  wide the model should be. Give your answer to 1 decimal place.

Glossary

add, addition (+)	Addition is the sum of two numbers or quantities.
adjacent (side)	Adjacent sides are next to each other and are joined by a common vertex.
algebra	Algebra is the branch of mathematics where symbols or letters are used to represent numbers.
amount	Amount means total.
angle: acute, obtuse, right, reflex	An angle is formed when two straight lines cross or meet each other at a point. The size of an angle is measured by the amount one line has been turned in relation to the other.

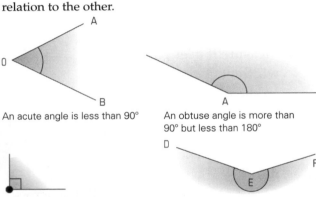

An acute angle is less than 90°

An obtuse angle is more than 90° but less than 180°

A right angle is a quarter of a turn, or 90°

A reflex angle is more than 180° but less than 360°

angles at a point	Angles at a point add up to 360°.

$a + b + c = 360°$

angles on a straight line	Angles on a straight line add up to 180°.

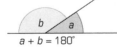

$a + b = 180°$

approximate, approximately	An approximate value is a value that is close to the actual value of a number.
approximately equal to (≈)	Approximately equal to means almost the same size.
area: square millimetre, square centimetre, square metre, square kilometre	The area of a surface is a measure of its size.
average	An average is a representative value of a set of data.
axis, axes	An axis is one of the lines used to locate a point in a coordinate system.
bar chart	A bar chart is a diagram that uses rectangles of equal width to display data. The frequency is given by the height of the rectangle.
bar-line graph	A bar-line graph is a diagram that uses lines to display data. The lengths of the lines are proportional to the frequencies.
base	The lower horizontal edge of a shape or solid is usually called the base. Similarly, the base of a solid is its lower face.

base

between	Between means in the space bounded by two limits.
brackets	Operations within brackets should be carried out first.
calculate, calculation	Calculate means work out using a mathematical procedure.
calculator	You can use a calculator to perform calculations.
cancel, cancellation	A fraction is cancelled down by dividing the numerator and denominator by a common factor. For example,

$$\frac{24}{40} = \frac{3}{5}$$

Glossary

capacity: litre
Capacity is a measure of the amount of liquid a 3-D shape will hold.

centre of rotation
The centre of rotation is the fixed point about which a rotation takes place.

certain
An event that is certain will definitely happen.

chance
Chance is the probability of something happening.

class interval
A class interval is a group that you put data into to make it easier to handle.

common factor
A common factor is a factor of two or more numbers.
For example, 2 is a common factor of 4 and 10.

compare
Compare means to assess the similarity of.

congruent
Congruent shapes are exactly the same shape and size.

consecutive
Consecutive means following on in order.
For example 2, 3 and 4 are consecutive integers.

construct
To construct means to draw a line, angle or shape accurately.

continue
Continue means carry on.

convert
Convert means to change.

coordinate pair
A coordinate pair is a pair of numbers that give the position of a point on a coordinate grid.
For example, (3, 2) means 3 units across and 2 units up.

coordinate point
A coordinate point is the point described by a coordinate pair.

coordinates
Coordinates are the numbers that make up a coordinate pair.

data	Data are pieces of information.
data collection sheet	A data collection sheet is a sheet used to collect data. It is sometimes a list of questions with tick boxes for collecting answers.
decimal number	A decimal number is a number written using a deimal point.
decimal place (d.p.)	Each column after the decimal point is called a decimal place. For example, 0.65 has two decimal places (2 d.p.)
degree (°)	A degree is a measure of turn. There are 360° in a full turn.
denominator	The denominator is the bottom number in a fraction. It shows how many parts there are in total.
difference	You find the difference between two amounts by subtracting one from the other.
digit	A digit is any of the numbers 0, 1, 2, 3, 4, 5, 6, 7, 8, 9.
direction	The direction is the orientation of a line in space.
distance	The distance between two points is the length of the line that joins them.
divide, division (÷)	Divide means share equally.
divisible, divisibility	A whole number is divisible by another if there is no remainder left.
divisor	The divisor is the number that does the dividing. For example, in 14 ÷ 2 = 7 the divisor is 2.
double, halve	Double means multiply by two. Halve means divide by two.

Glossary

edge (of solid)	An edge is a line along which two faces of a solid meet.
equal (sides, angles)	Equal sides are the same length. Equal angles are the same size.
equally likely	Events are equally likely if they have the same probability.
equals (=)	Equals means having exactly the same value or size.
equation	An equation is a statement using an = sign to link two expressions.
equivalent, equivalence	Equivalent fractions are fractions with the same value.
estimate	An estimate is an approximate answer.
evaluate	Evaluate means find the value of an expression.
exact, exactly	Exact means completely accurate. For example, three divides into six exactly.
experiment	An experiment is a test or investigation to gather evidence for or against a theory.
expression	An expression is a collection of numbers and symbols linked by operations but not including an equals sign.
face	A face is a flat surface of a solid.
factor	A factor is a number that divides exactly into another number. For example, 3 and 7 are factors of 21.
fair	In a fair experiment there is no bias towards any particular outcome.
fraction	A fraction is a way of describing a part of a whole. $\frac{2}{5}$

frequency	Frequency is the number of times something occurs.
frequency diagram	A frequency diagram uses bars to display grouped data. The height of each bar gives the frequency of the group, and there is no space between the bars.
function	A function is a rule. For example, $+2$, -3, $\times 4$ and $\div 5$ are all functions.
function machine	A function machine links an input value to an output value by performing a function.
generalise	Generalise means formulate a general statement or rule.
generate	Generate means produce.
graph	A graph is a diagram that shows a relationship between variables.
greater than (>)	Greater than means more than. For example $4 > 3$.
grid	A grid is used as a background to plot coordinate points. It is usually squared.
height	Height is the vertical distance from the base to the top of a shape.
highest common factor (HCF)	The highest common factor is the largest factor that is common to two or more numbers. For example, the HCF of 12 and 8 is 4.
horizontal	Horizontal means flat and level with the ground.
hundredth	A hundredth is 1 out of 100. For example 0.05 has 5 hundredths.
impossible	An event is impossible if it definitely cannot happen.

Glossary

improper fraction
An improper fraction is a fraction where the numerator is greater than the denominator. For example, $\frac{8}{5}$

increase, decrease
Increase means make greater.
Decrease means make less.

input, output
Input is data fed into a machine or process. Output is the data produced by a machine or process.

integer
An integer is a positive or negative whole number (including zero). The integers are: ..., -3, -2, -1, 0, 1, 2, 3, ...

interpret
You interpret data whenever you make sense of it.

intersect, intersection
Two lines intersect at the point, or points, that they cross.

intersection

interval
An interval is the size of a class or group in a frequency table.

inverse
An inverse operation has the opposite effect to the original operation. For example, multiplication is the inverse of division.

label
A label is a description of a diagram or object.

length: millimetre, centimetre, metre, kilometre; mile, foot, inch
Length is a measure of distance. It is often used to describe one dimension of a shape.

less than (<)
Less than means smaller than.
For example, 3 is less than 4 or 3 < 4.

likelihood
Likelihood is the probability of an event happening.

likely
An event is likely if it will happen more often than not.

line of symmetry
A line of symmetry is a line about which a 2-D shape can be folded so that one half of the shape fits exactly on the other half.

line symmetry	A shape has line symmetry if it has a line of symmetry.
line	A line joins two points.
lowest common multiple (LCM)	The lowest common multiple is the smallest multiple that is common to two or more numbers. For example the LCM of 4 and 6 is 12.
lowest terms	A fraction is in its lowest terms when the numerator and denominator have no common factors.
mapping	A mapping is a rule that can be applied to a set of numbers to give another set of numbers.
mass: gram, kilogram; ounce, pound	Mass is a measure of the weight of an object.
mean	The mean is an average value found by adding all the data values and dividing by the number of pieces of data.
measure	When you measure something you find the size of it.
median	The median is the average value which is the middle value when the data is arranged in size order.
mirror line	A mirror line is a line of symmetry. 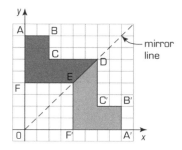
mixed number	A mixed number has a whole number part and a fraction part. For example, $3\frac{1}{2}$ is a mixed number.

Glossary

modal class	The modal class is the most commonly occurring class when the data is grouped. It is the class with the highest frequency.
mode	The mode is an average which is the data value that occurs most often.
multiple	A multiple of an integer is the product of that integer and any other. For example, these are multiples of 6: $6 \times 4 = 24$ and $6 \times 12 = 72$.
multiply, multiplication ($\times$)	Multiplication is the operation of combining two numbers or quantities to form a product.
nearest	Nearest means the closest value.
negative	A negative number is a number less than zero.
net	A net is a 2-D arrangement that can be folded to form a solid shape.
nth term	The nth term is the general term of a sequence.
numerator	The numerator is the top number in a fraction. It shows how many parts you are dealing with.
object, image	The object is the original shape before a transformation. An image is the same shape after a transformation.
operation	An operation is a rule for processing numbers or objects. The basic operations are addition, subtraction, multiplication and division.
opposite (sides, angles)	Opposite means across from.
order	To order means to arrange according to size or importance.

order of operations	The conventional order of operations is BIDMAS: brackets first, then indicies, then division and multiplication, then addition and subtraction.
order of rotation symmetry	The order of rotation symmetry is the number of times that a shape will fit on to itself during a full turn.
origin	The origin is the point where the x- and y-axes cross, that is $(0, 0)$.
outcome	An outcome is the result of a trial or experiment.
parallel	Two lines that always stay the same distance apart are parallel. Parallel lines never cross or meet.
partition; part	To partition means to split a number into smaller amounts, or parts. For example, 57 could be split into 50 + 7, or 40 + 17.
percentage (%)	A percentage is a fraction expressed as the number of parts per hundred.
perimeter	The perimeter of a shape is the distance around it. It is the total length of the edges.
perpendicular	Two lines are perpendicular to each other if they meet at a right angle.
pie chart	A pie chart uses a circle to display data. The angle at the centre of a sector is proportional to the frequency.
place value	The place value is the value of a digit in a decimal number. For example, in 3.65 the digit 6 has a value of 6 tenths.
polygon: pentagon, hexagon, octagon	A polygon is a closed shape with three or more straight edges.

A pentagon has five sides

A hexagon has six sides.

An octagon has eight sides.

Glossary

positive
A positive number is greater than zero.

predict
Predict means forecast in advance.

prime
A prime number is a number that has exactly two different factors.

probability
Probability is a measure of how likely an event is.

probability scale
A probability scale is a line numbered 0 to 1 or 0% to 100% on which you place an event based on its probability.

product
The product is the result of a multiplication.

proportion
Proportion compares the size of a part to the size of a whole. You can express a proportion as a fraction, decimal or percentage.

protractor (angle measurer)
A protractor is an instrument for measuring angles in degrees.

quadrant
A coordinate grid is divided into four quadrants by the x- and y-axes.

quadrilateral: arrowhead, kite, parallelogram, rectangle, rhombus, square, trapezium
A quadrilateral is a polygon with four sides.

rectangle

All angles are right angles.

parallelogram

Two pairs of parallel sides.

kite

Two pairs of adjacent sides equal.

rhombus

All sides the same length. Opposite angles equal.

square

All sides and angles equal.

trapezium

One pair of parallel sides.

questionnaire	A questionnaire is a list of questions used to gather information in a survey.
quotient	A quotient is the result of a division.
random	A selection is random if each object or number is equally likely to be chosen.
range	The range is the difference between the largest and smallest values in a set of data.
ratio	Ratio compares the size of one part with the size of another part.
reflect, reflection	A reflection is a transformation in which corresponding points in the object and the image are the same distance from the mirror line.
reflection symmetry	A shape has reflection symmetry if it has a line of symmetry.
regular	A regular polygon has equal sides and equal angles.
relationship	A relationship is a link between objects or numbers.
remainder	A remainder is the amount left over when one quantity is exactly divided by another. For example, $9 \div 4 = 2$ remainder 1 or 2 r 1.
represent	You represent data whenever you display it in the form of a diagram.
rotate, rotation	A rotation is a transformation in which every point in the object turns through the same angle relative to a fixed point.
rotation symmetry	A shape has rotation symmetry if when turned it fits onto itself more than once during a full turn.

Glossary

round

You round a number by expressing it to a given degree of accuracy. For example, 639 is 600 to the nearest 100 and 640 to the nearest 10.

To round to one decimal place means to round to the nearest tenth. For example 12.47 is 12.5 to 1 d.p.

rule

A rule describes the link between objects or numbers. For example, the rule linking 2 and 6 may be +4 or ×3.

ruler

A ruler is an instrument for measuring lengths.

sequence

A sequence is a set of numbers or objects that follow a rule.

shape

A shape is made by a line or lines drawn on a surface, or by putting surfaces together.

side (of 2-D shape)

A side is a line segment joining vertices.

sign

A sign is a symbol used to denote an operation.

simplest form

A fraction (or ratio) is in its simplest form when the numerator and denominator (or parts of the ratio) have no common factors.

For example, $\frac{3}{5}$ is expressed in its simplest form.

simplify

To simplify an expression you gather all like terms together into a single term.

sketch

A sketch shows the general shape of a graph or diagram.

solid (3-D) shape: cube, cuboid, prism, pyramid,

A solid is a shape formed in three-dimensional space.

cube   cuboid   prism

six square faces   six rectangular faces   the end faces are constant

solution (of an equation)

The solution of an equation is the value of the variable that makes the equation true.

solve (an equation)	To solve an equation you need to find the value of the variable that will make the equation true.
spin, spinner	A spinner is an instrument for creating random outcomes, usually in probability experiments.

square-based pyramid, tetrahedron

pyramid

tetrahedron

square-based pyramid

the faces meet at a common vertex angles equal.

all faces are equilateral triangles

the base is a square

square number, squared	If you multiply a number by itself the result is a square number. For example 25 is a square number because $5^2 = 5 \times 5 = 25$.
square root	A square root is a number that when multiplied by itself is equal to a given number. For example, $\sqrt{25} = 5$, because $5 \times 5 = 25$.
statistic, statistics	Statistics is the collection, display and analysis of information.
straight-line graph	When coordinate points lie in a straight line they form a straight-line graph. It is the graph of a linear equation.

substitute	When you substitute you replace part of an expression with its value.
subtract, subtraction (−)	Subtraction is the operation that finds the difference in

Glossary

	size between two numbers.
sum	The sum is the total and is the result of an addition.
surface, surface area	The surface area of a solid is the total area of its faces.
survey	A survey is an investigation to find information.
symbol	A symbol is a letter, number or other mark that represents a number or an operation.
symmetrical	A shape is symmetrical if it is unchanged after a rotation or reflection.
table	A table is an arrangement of information, numbers or letters usually in rows and columns.
tally	You use a tally mark to represent an object when you collect data. Tally marks are usually made in groups of five to make it easier to count them.
temperature: degrees Celsius, degrees Fahrenheit	Temperature is a measure of how hot something is.
tenth	A tenth is 1 out of 10 or $\frac{1}{10}$. For example 0.5 has 5 tenths.
term	A term is a number or object in a sequence. It is also part of an expression.
thousandth	A thousandth is 1 out of 1000 or $\frac{1}{1000}$. For example, 0.002 has 2 thousandths.
three-dimensional (3-D)	Any solid shape in three-dimensional.
total	The total is the result of an addition.
transformation	A transformation moves a shape from one place to another.
translate, translation	A translation is a transformation in which every point in an object moves the same distance and direction.

triangle: equilateral, isosceles, scalene, right-angled	It is a sliding movement. A triangle is a polygon with three sides.

equilateral

three equal sides

isosceles

two equal sides

scalene

no equal sides

right-angled

one angle is 90

two-dimensional (2-D)	A flat shape has two dimensions, length and width or base and height.
unknown	An unknown is a variable. You can often find its value by solving an equation.
value	The value is the amount an expression or variable is worth.
variable	A variable is a symbol that can take any value.
vertex, vertices	A vertex of a shape is a point at which two or more edges meet.

vertex

vertical	Vertical means straight up and down.
vertically opposite angles	When two straight lines cross they form two pairs of equal angles called vertically opposite angles.

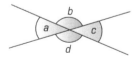

$a = c$ $b = d$

whole	The whole is the full amount.
width	Width is a dimension of an object describing how

Glossary

x-axis, y-axis

wide it is.
On a coordinate grid,
the x-axis is usually the
horizontal axis and the
y-axis is usually the
vertical axis.

x-coordinate, y-coordinate

The x-coordinate is the distance along the x-axis.
The y-coordinate is the distance along the y-axis.
For example, (-2, -3) is -2 along the x-axis and -3 along
the y-axis.

zero

Zero is nought or nothing.
A zero place holder is used to
show the place value of other
digits in a number.